THE

LANDMARK

HANDBOOK

The Egyptian House, Penzance.

THE
LANDMARK
HANDBOOK

1977
(Reprinted 1987)

PUBLISHED BY THE LANDMARK TRUST
SHOTTESBROOKE, MAIDENHEAD, BERKSHIRE

Dunira Street, Comrie

The Pineapple

Hill House

Rosslyn Castle

Saddell
Tangy Mill

Wellbrook
Beetling Mill

The Old Place
of Monreith

The Banqueting House

The Old Grammar School
The Culloden Tower

The Music Room

Beamsley Hospital

Calverley Old Hall

Cawood Castle

Edale Mill

The Chateau

The Bath Tower

Ty Capel & Ty Coch

10 North Street,
Cromford

Plas Uchaf

Alton Station
The Pavilion
Tixall Gatehouse

The Stand

Appleton
Water Tower

The House
of Correction

34 High Street,
Ironbridge

Lynch Lodge

Manor Farm

The New Inn
The Martello Tower

Maes-yr-Onen

Stockwell Farm
Shelwick Court

The Tower,
Canons Ashby

Purton Green

15 Tower Hill,
St Davids

Church Cottage

Warden Abbey

The
Gothic Temple

Tower Hill Lodge

St Mary's Lane;
The Abbey Gatehouse

Clytha Castle

The Old Parsonage

Monkton Old Hall

45a Cloth Fair

Marshal Wade's House;
Elton House

Woodspring Priory
The Captain's Flat

The Old Hall

Lundy

Gurney Street
Manor

Stogursey Castle

The Wardrobe

Hole Cottage

The Library
Coombe
The College

The Priest's House

Fox Hall

Laughton
Place

Shute Gatehouse

Luttrell's Tower

Wortham Manor

Lettaford

Margells

Woodsford
Castle

Whiteford Temple
The Danescombe
Mine

Endsleigh

Peters Tower

The Egyptian
House

Fort Clonque

The Nicolle Tower

Contents

Introduction

THE LANDMARK TRUST is a charity which rescues buildings in distress and then tries to give them life and a future, mostly by letting them for holidays. In this way a constant succession of different people can actually stay in historic or important buildings. By living there, however briefly, people get far more out of a place than just by looking at it; they can study it at leisure, be there early and late, in all lights and weathers, and get the feel of its surroundings.

About 10,000 people a year now stay in sixty or so of our places, each carefully chosen and with a special atmosphere and point of its own. These are not large figures, but we believe that by using buildings in this way—where possible combined with ordinary public access—the maximum number of people get the most from them; and that many visitors who go just for a holiday come back with their interest aroused in what they have found there.

Often the best for this purpose are those minor but handsome buildings which tend to fall through the preservation net. Ornamental, vernacular, industrial, even military, they are the product of much thought and care, part of our history and of the scene, but their original function has disappeared. They cannot be saved from vandals, demolition or decay unless a new use can be found for them. To turn them into permanent homes is either impossible, or involves changes and additions which would spoil them, but which people making a short stay do not need. As the weekend or holiday retreats of individual owners they would lie for most of the year empty and unenjoyed; let by us they are occupied almost all the time, and an income is produced for their maintenance. They are of every age and style, in all parts of the country, and some of the best are in towns. Many of them have come to us through schemes undertaken with the National Trust. other charities, or with local authorities.

Inevitably we find ourselves owning cottages and houses, but we try not to take out of the "housing stock" any which would have made permanent homes, and we do in fact have about thirty long-term tenants. Slightly to our surprise, letting a building for short periods, especially outside so-called holiday areas, often pleases our neighbours rather than the reverse, by producing a succession of interested newcomers, some of whom find themselves caught up in the life of the place, particularly in winter.

Many of the buildings we tackle are desperate cases, in the last stages of decay. To rescue these may need perseverance just as much as money. Sometimes a building has become stranded without access; more often it is owned or controlled by someone who feels that it would be a nuisance to him if it were restored and used. In fact our sort of use, because it is unassertive, and need not involve outworks such as garages or gardens—or indeed any land at all outside the actual building—is usually far less of a nuisance and worry to an owner than any other solution. We try to persuade people of this, but we have had regrettable defeats, where we could have afforded the cost of saving a building, and where once saved it would have given pleasure and edification for many years.

Rather in the same way, our problem when restoring a building is not just how to find the money to do enough; it is also how to avoid doing too much. We do not like buildings in what Queen Victoria used to call "A very high state of preservation"; but there is always pressure from architects, builders or local authorities to make the building perfect, to renew and replace. This is understandable; architects and builders do not want to be blamed later for defects, and the framers of byelaws must be propitiated. But often the result is a building which has lost all texture, both visual and historical, and which looks as uneasy as a schoolboy cleaned up by a tough mother. This is most marked with derelict timber-framed buildings. To repair these is like patching a cobweb; and although we set our face against conjectural restoration, the urge is often irresistible to replace missing timbers whose original appearance can be deduced with certainty, instead of carrying out such repairs in a different material which is what a purist would do. We have made mistakes and we have overdone it here and there; nevertheless in European Architectural Heritage Year we did, to our surprise, win eleven awards, several more than any other recipient in Britain, including the Government.

One of the things which most damages an interior is replacing the doors. However worn and tiresome, they should be mended rather than replaced. But ever tougher fire regulations make this and other desirable aims increasingly difficult. Of course we do not want to burn people, but it is a shame, when more is now known about the correct treatment of old buildings, that new fire regulations should often make much of it impossible to carry out.

Inside, our places are not made luxurious or smart; they are simply put in good order and made as practical and comfortable as their nature allows. We take trouble when furnishing them, aiming to please the eye and interest people without being extravagant: almost all the furniture is old and good, simple and carefully chosen—indeed we find ourselves rescuing furniture in distress as well as buildings. Most of the curtains are specially designed and printed for each place. The rugs and carpets are exceptional, if seldom in their first youth. All the pictures, however humble, have some special reason for being there. We are trying to preserve and restore not only the buildings but also the outlook on life which created them; very often that too was a work of art.   Until 1976 most of this was the province of Mrs. Sonia Rolt.

We also give each Landmark a shelf of books to do with it and its surroundings and with the environment in general. These are not just historical or explanatory but include fiction (and poetry) with local associations. For each building we are also assembling an album of historical notes, plans and photographs; and, in case it does not rain, there are large scale maps of the district marking the footpaths. A stay in a Landmark is meant to be not just a holiday but an experience, of a mildly elevating kind.

Attempting all this—and maintaining it in buildings constantly occupied— is not easy, or indeed always achieved. The work is done by a small and rather scattered staff, almost all part-time, and grateful thanks are due to them, especially to our caretakers.

Just who stays in our places? Alas, we seldom meet them, but we know a good deal about them because each Landmark has a logbook in which visitors can write whatever they like for the benefit of their successors. Here they display great enterprise and good humour. They find and record the most fascinating things to see and do—far more varied than we could ever have suggested to them. Most people make for themselves some discovery or other. They drive around rather disappointingly much, but some are content just to be there, and allow their car to have a holiday as well; and a noble few come by public transport, which is quite adequate for several of our places. At Landmarks in towns our visitors greatly enjoy having their own front door instead of staying in a hotel. A few come from abroad, particularly from Australia (touched off by an article which appeared there called "The Englishman's home is his Pineapple"). A surprising number are not on holiday at all, but come to do or to study something specific. Many come again, and again; one heroic party stayed five times at Purton Green. Many try one Landmark after another.

They enjoy themselves a lot, particularly at Christmas; it is clear from what they write that sometimes they give vent to song, even dance. They are amazingly little trouble to us, or to the neighbours where there are any. Some of them write so beautifully, and sound so charming, that one longs to meet them, almost with a view to matrimony. A visitor at Clytha left a recipe for chestnut soup. Another, at Peasenhall, wrote "A terrible draught comes up from the cellar, catching me in a very delicate spot when I sit waiting for my dinner" on behalf of her bulldog. One family hid stamps for the next young collectors to find. Some of the children have never seen an open fire and find it as surprising as a wild animal in the room; children indeed write in the logbooks with enviable candour—"The shopkeeper is very pleasant after she has got over her shyness"; "We visited Looe, not a very nice town"; "I would not recommend a day on the river as it is £1.25 an hour and the boats are terribly scruffy". Though each party occupies a Landmark for a very short time, the logbook links them with those who come before and after, and gives to them and to the place a sense of continuity. The logbooks are a marvellous reward to us for our labour.

Our charges are shown on a separate sheet which, if this handbook has lost its copy, can be had from the Secretary. It is difficult for us to compare our prices with those of other people since, so far as we know, nobody else offers quite the same thing; but our places seem always very fully booked. We have advertised hardly ever, the news of us spreading by hearsay. We much prefer this, since people will on the whole only recommend the Landmark to those of their friends whom they think will enjoy it. In this way disappointments are avoided.

In addition to our work with buildings, we have also carried out schemes for the removal of eyesores and wirescapes (one by way of an invisible memorial to Mr. L. T. C. Rolt, a man who never cared to be too visible himself) and we do of course administer the island of Lundy. This is by far the most demanding and expensive of all our projects, but at the same time by far the most visited.

Of the money which we spend 7% has come from visitors, and 9% from the Historic Buildings Council, the Tourist Boards and local authorities, to each of which we are most grateful. Almost all the remainder comes from an older and more general charity also started by my wife and myself. This is the Manifold Trust, which distributes its income mainly to environmental causes of one sort or another. We have not written about the Manifold before, but experience has shown that to remain unknown has disadvantages—indeed dangers—for a charity, and therefore we now summarise its work on page 161.

About twelve years ago the Manifold began to grow, and we were then able to start the Landmark, primarily to supplement in a small way the work of the National Trust, on whose head office committees I have been honoured to sit for many years. Certain projects, mainly the small, the desperate, or the peculiar, cannot for one reason or another be undertaken by the National Trust. We had long wanted to tackle these, and it is dreadful to think of all the buildings of our sort, particularly on the canal system, which were destroyed before we were in a position to do anything about them.

Those who care about our surroundings fight under a handicap. When a fine building is demolished, or a fine place spoilt, that is the end of the matter; whereas the destroyer, if foiled, can always try again. To win at all we have to win every time, whereas the forces of destruction need only win once. We are inevitably on the defensive, appearing indeed to fight a rearguard action only; and it is all too easy for those who destroy to represent those who care as backward-looking and obstructive. But the reverse is the truth. Material progress has at least meant that we are no longer obliged to foul our surroundings in order to survive. Indeed it now seems that we cannot survive if we do. It is those who still preach cheapness at any price who are beginning to look old-fashioned; while those who preach against waste, whether of buildings or other resources, are modern. Far from being something restrictive, preservation is now constructive, and creative as well, and those who care about the environment are in fact in the vanguard of progress.

Moreover the Landmark Trust is not just engaged in preservation. It is trying to make "preservation" unnecessary by opening the eyes of as many people as possible. Indeed our aim is to rouse people's interest in their surroundings in the widest sense—their surroundings both in space and time. The environment is not just a film set. History is part of the environment; so is the way people live, their scale of values, and how they treat the rest of creation. We hope that every day some of our 10,000 guests, as they set up house in one or other of our places, will begin to feel that "here a man may, without much molestation, be thinking what he is, whence he came, what he has done, and to what the King has called him".

John Smith

Staying in Landmarks

OUR BUILDINGS (except one or two on Lundy) are available, and meant to be used, all the year round, not just in summer; all have heating of some sort, and wherever possible there is an open fire in the living room as well.

Almost all have electricity (for which there is no extra charge, even in winter) for lighting, heating, hot water and cooking. These places also have electric irons and kettles and heated towel rails in the bathrooms. The remainder (Fort Clonque, the Martello Tower, and most of the buildings on Lundy) have calor gas. All (except Tibbetts on Lundy) have w.c.'s; all have bathrooms (except some on Lundy; and Appleton and the Martello, which have showers); all have refrigerators.

All beds (except the stow-away beds) have interior-sprung mattresses, but some bunks have mattresses of thick Dunlopillo. There are plenty of blankets.

We do not supply pillowcases, sheets, or towels. We do supply bath mats, and drying-up cloths (except on Lundy); and all cleaning equipment, including a vacuum cleaner or carpet sweeper.

Each place is looked after by a caretaker who will have it ready for your arrival, but we do hope and expect that you will leave it as clean as you can.

Really well-behaved dogs are welcome (but not at Appleton or on Lundy, where the temptations are too great; nor at the Music Room, Marshal Wade's House or the Egyptian House).

We are well aware how upsetting a spoilt holiday can be, and so we do our level best to see that all goes well. However, our places are scattered and some are remote; management is not easy. Therefore if, sometimes, something does go wrong we hope that you will be tolerant and understanding.

Booking

Please first read all the notes and conditions in our letting leaflet.

Booking is best done on the telephone (Monday to Friday, 9.30-5.30), since we can then answer any questions immediately, and can discuss alternatives if your first choice is not available.

For **Lundy** please read the separate leaflet "Staying on Lundy" and then telephone Woolacombe (0271) 870870 or, which will take much longer, write to the Administrator, Col. R. C. Gilliat, Lundy, Bristol Channel, via Ilfracombe, North Devon.

For the **Harp Inn** please telephone New Radnor 655, or write to the Manager, The Harp Inn, Old Radnor, Presteigne, Powys.

The Harp is run like any other small hotel, that is to say rooms can be booked for any period, and the Manager will tell you the prices.

For **All Other Landmarks** telephone **Littlewick Green** (062-882) 5925, or write to the Landmark Trust, Shottesbrooke, Maidenhead, Berkshire.

We prefer to let for at least a week, but "out of season" all our places (except some on Lundy) may be taken for shorter periods, including **Weekends**.

The Old Hall
Croscombe, Nr. Wells, Somerset

ORIGINALLY THE GREAT HALL of a medieval manor house built by the Palton family about 1420, this building has for the last 250 years been a Baptist chapel—the

baptisms taking place at first in the River Sheppey nearby. It lies just north of the church (a handsome one, as usual in Somerset), and looks into a small, most

The Old Hall

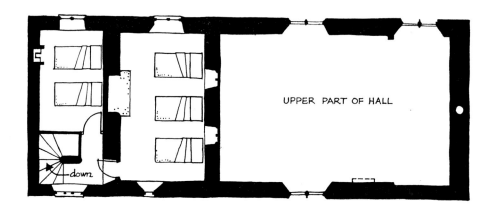

FIRST FLOOR

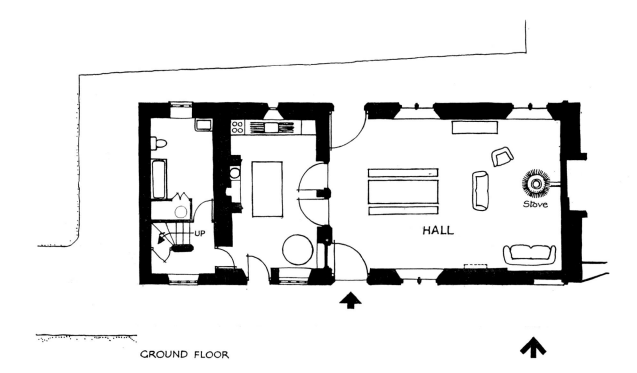

GROUND FLOOR

The Old Hall

tranquil enclosure, part garden and part graveyard.

The Baptists, but for whom the building must have disappeared, made a number of harmless alterations—raising of window sills, blocking of doors, a flat ceiling etc. Removal of these, and the repairing of this somewhat tottering structure, have revealed quite a grand hall with a fine arch-braced open roof. A medieval light bracket has also appeared, which had been boxed in rather than destroyed, and on it are the arms of William Palton, (who died in 1449) impaling Wellington, and of his brother Robert impaling Botreaux. We have turned the service end of the hall into bedrooms and kitchen, just simple rooms of wood and stone.

Alton Station
Nr. Stoke-on-Trent, Staffordshire

FOR SOME TIME we had been looking for a suitable small railway station, since there is hardly any class of building which is disappearing more rapidly. Alton is a most notable example, the only Italianate station in Staffordshire, and we are indeed grateful to this enlightened County Council for conveying it to us in 1970. The railway has gone, at least for the present; but in its heyday the platforms took 12-coach excursion trains from the Potteries.

Its architect is unknown, though it has been ascribed, improbably, to A. W. Pugin. Built by the North Staffordshire Railway (the "Knotty") to a befitting standard for the Earl of Shrewsbury, then owner of Alton Towers, it lies in marvellous surroundings, both beautiful and interesting. Pugin's Alton Castle rises out of the trees across the valley of the Churnet, like

something from the Carinthia of Dornford Yates; and Alton Towers itself, with its famous nineteenth-century garden, lies immediately behind. Beyond the up platform lies the long abandoned canal from Froghall to Uttoxeter.

During our work on the house a disused flue was found to have been blocked by stuffing it with porters' waistcoats. The plumbing which we have installed makes a strange chuffing sound—doubtless the craving of this house for the sound and smell of great engines wreathed in steam. Our caretaker, Mrs. Bowers, was one of the last passengers to travel on the line. She still has her ticket from Leek to Alton (fare 3/-) dated 2 Jan. 1965.

From the logbook
"We walked along the line to Oakamoor

and in the Lord Nelson there are displayed the boots worn by Sir Stanley Matthews in the 1953 Cup Final".

"A nice E. Nesbit atmosphere".

"We met some schoolboys out on a run who took us into their incredible castle and gave us a view of the valley from a door in its side".

"Indelible memories to take home".

"Mine has been a sentimental journey; I returned with my wife and family, including grandchildren, to this beautiful spot after an absence of 29 years. I was Station Master here from November 1939 to October 1946. The station staff consisted of Station Master, 2 porters, one porter/signalman. The Station Master's salary was £230 per annum. The peak number of trains dealt with in one day numbered 25. The Signal Box was the only one of its kind on the North Staffordshire Railway and at one time had window boxes all around it tended by the Earl of Shrewsbury's gardeners.

At the outbreak of war in 1939 Alton Towers was taken over by the army. The Unit to make the biggest impact was 123 Officer Cadet Training Unit, Royal Horse Artillery (Lt. Col. Burns). In their wake came fifteen West End tailors who set up establishments in all local public houses. Wives and girl friends of officers and cadets took up all available accommodation in the hotels and private houses. The OCTU had

a special train to Trawsfynydd each month to the firing ranges and took all their equipment including field guns with them.

The winters of 1940 and 1947 were exceptionally hard with snow drifts up to six feet deep. Milk was frozen solid in the churns.

We have had a wonderful welcome back and we have been delighted to be reunited with our friends."

"We carried our baby Nancy in her push chair along the abandoned railway. She looked like the Queen of Sheba borne on some triumphal expedition through virgin lands."

"The birds at evening are marvellous— I hear them as I write this on our last evening here."

At the Opening in 1849   *by L. V. Wood*

Alton Station

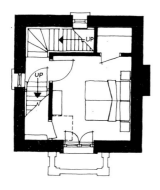

FIRST FLOOR

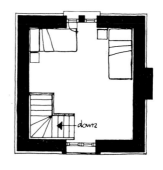

SECOND FLOOR

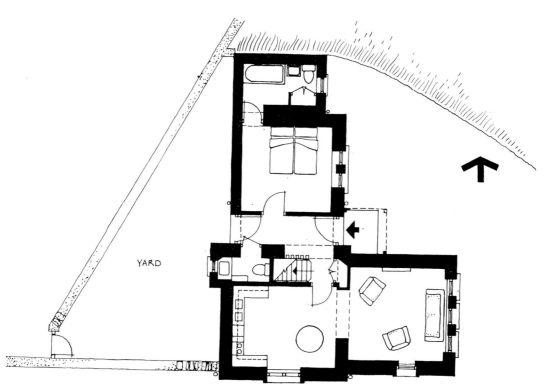

YARD

PLATFORM

Platform edge

GROUND FLOOR PLAN

The Bath Tower

Caernarfon, Gwynedd

THIS IS ONE of the late thirteenth-century towers of the medieval town wall, facing the Menai Strait. It is said to derive its name from its use in the nineteenth century by Lord Anglesey as a base for sea bathing; certainly in that century the two great windows in the living room were made. These, in deep embrasures, look along the outside of the town wall towards the castle in one direction, and across the Strait in the other. Here you can have your cake and eat it—the sea at your feet in front, with not a vehicle in sight; and the pleasures of an interesting town at your back.

The tower had been empty for some long time when we bought it, and we have since bought a short stretch of the town wall to one side. Both entrances are very striking —one along a narrow alley from the street

behind, and the other from the sea wall. On the floor below the living room, reached by a spiral stair, there is a single very large room in which several people can sleep, like soldiers of the Edwardian garrison. It is here that we found, and have left, the tremendous antlers so charmingly referred to in the logbook. If, however, there are only two of you, then you can ignore this room altogether, and sleep in seclusion at the top of the tower, with just the sky and the battlements.

From the logbook

"An eleven hour journey terminated outside no. 10 Church Street—a conventional residential street—a slight feeling of disappointment—until we set off down the pitch-dark alley under the towering wall,

The Bath Tower

up the winding stone stairs. Our tiredness fell away as we explored the Tower — all our expectations fulfilled".

"A medieval atmosphere has been achieved without the discomforts of that period".

"We found a lack of boats for hire, but after chatting up the pilots on the pilot boat had a very enjoyable four hours trip to put a pilot on board an Esso tanker".

"I like the curtains very much".

"Hymn singing in the square, Sunday evenings at 8.30, is well worth attending".

"We put 4 children, all under nine years old, in the dungeon which they thoroughly enjoyed".

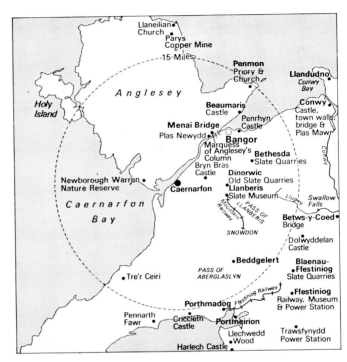

"We find we are the first group of students to stay here, seven girls . . . We thought that the antlers in the big bedroom would be less frightening for children if light colourful clothing were hung on them—we hung our scarves, hats and nightdresses up in this way . . . We went to Snowdon prepared with our emergency rations of Mars Bars and Dextrosol—we even considered exposure bags—having been warned of the sudden mists. We were extremely lucky with the weather and so made frequent stops to rest and eat, much to the amusement of our fellow climbers".

"The Bath Tower is very rewarding, quiet and private with its own scale of natural sounds—birds, children, grownups exchanging greetings in the evening, and high up the scale the fine screeching of swifts".

"The quickest way to walk into open country from here is along the old L. & N.W. line from the slate quay by the castle . . . A footpath leaves the shore by the disused church at Llanfaglan . . . We were chased by bullocks on the footpath and the farmer explained their behaviour by saying that they did not see many people".

"My family, grandma and I all enjoyed it very much here and found it very interesting watching the gulls".

"Visits to Wylfa power station can only be arranged on written application 'quoting an organisation in whom we would have some confidence such as the Scouts or WVS' as the polite CEGB man told us".

"Caernarvon is the local centre for about five bus companies. The Byzantine complexity of their operations finds its key in the Crosville timetable (at 5p a real public service). A determined organiser could clearly go far".

"The Bath Tower far exceeded our expectations in both impact and comfort".

"A rainy Friday was filled in by a visit to Bangor City Baths. When we asked the

The Bath Tower

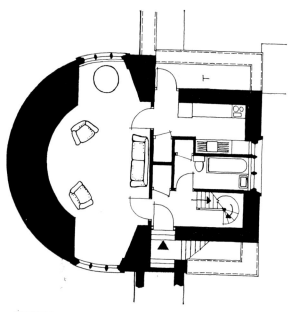

SECOND FLOOR

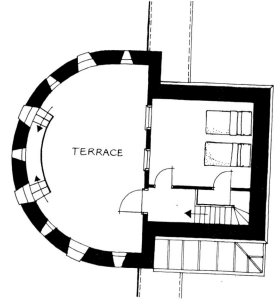

TERRACE

THIRD FLOOR

MENAI STRAITS

FORESHORE

SEA WALL

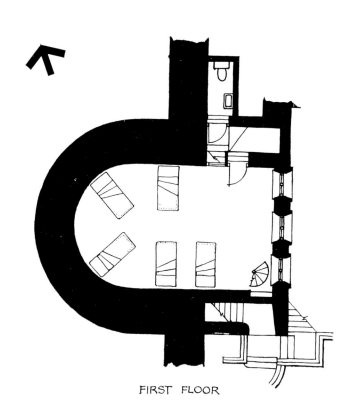

FIRST FLOOR

The Bath Tower

length of a period we were told 'When the Lord made time, he made plenty of it' ''.

"The library was a complete surprise and was particularly enjoyed when we were alone".

"Attended the Bryncir fatstock sale; extraordinary sights and smells and lots of action".

"The Bath Tower is a splendid place to be in; we felt at home the very moment we entered and every day looked forward to coming back to it after the day's excursion".

"At this time of year the best approach to Snowdon is up the so-called Beddgelert route. It is in the sun and free from snow. It is also out of the prevailing wind; on a clear sunny March day I could strip to the waist. But G. Borrow could never have got his daughter up that route, however many Welsh songs he sang her on the way. Ireland was clearly visible".

"We found Portmeirion expensive and rather tatty, but were pleased to have a glimpse of Clough Williams-Ellis himself, doing some pruning".

"To have lived in a building, if only for one short week, whose traditions reach so far back in history has been a worthwhile experience".

"We walked to Lleyn Llydaw and saw the peak where King Arthur fought his final fatal battle with the Saxons, after which his body was carried down to Llydaw and borne away to Avalon by a barge containing three beautiful women".

39-45 Cloth Fair
Smithfield, London E.C.1

This group of seventeenth, eighteenth and nineteenth century buildings, next to the church of St. Bartholomew the Great, was bought by us in 1970. No. 41 is said to be the only house in the City of London to have escaped the Great Fire of 1666 and all subsequent disasters. No 40 is still occupied by a cloth merchant, with nurses from St. Bartholomew's Hospital living over the shop.

We have repaired no 45, and have turned its upper part into living accommodation for permanent tenants. There is a great deal of work still to do to the rest of the group, but we hope that in due course it will be possible for visitors to stay here, and from here to explore the City at their leisure.

Church Cottage
Llandygwydd, Cardigan, Dyfed

CHURCH COTTAGE is early Victorian, just beginning to be Gothic, and built of Cilgerran slate. It is next to the church (rebuilt in 1857 by R. J. Withers of Cheltenham) of a small village five miles East of Cardigan, in a hilly, well-wooded countryside of small farms.

Though less than a mile from the main Newcastle Emlyn to Cardigan road, Llandygwydd is extremely quiet; there is, in fact, a small road between the cottage and the church, but little goes along it. The theatre in Cardigan is recommended; so is the coracle race from Cenarth to Llechrydd on Easter Monday. The South sweep of Cardigan Bay, where there are good beaches, is less than ten miles away; however the point of Church Cottage is not to dash about, but simply to be there, in this distant and unremarkable part of Wales, and feel what it is like.

From the logbook

"We arrived from Welwyn Garden City (Herts) to find the cottage spick and span".

"Here is a list of the birds we have seen without really trying . . .".

"Sea trout can be bought at the Post Office in Cenarth".

"The laburnum hedges have been at their finest this week. Locals say surpassing anything seen for many years".

"At Llanbyther a horse fair of ancient origin is held on the last Thursday in each month".

"October is a lovely time to be here . . . The fire is really good once you have the knack. We had blackberries every day".

"Afternoon tea establishments seem fairly rare".

Church Cottage

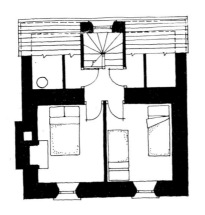

FIRST FLOOR

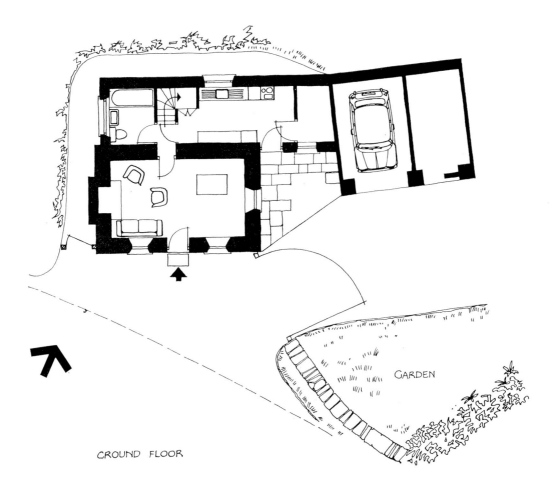

GARDEN

GROUND FLOOR

14

Church Cottage

"We brought our dinghy and sailed on most days in Cardigan estuary".

"Our main interest has been birds and butterflies ... The children have recorded several firsts".

"We would like to thank the Landmark Trust for an excellent week and we are sorry if we could not clear up all the confetti".

"A pleasant walk is up the river Cych. The slopes of the valley are beautiful now that the larch is green".

"In December no need for a car at all—better to use your feet over the many miles of empty roads, footpaths and water-laden tracks".

"It was a joy to see harts tongue ferns growing in the bank outside the bathroom window".

"We fished every night at Cenarth".

"We found lots and lots to do and never

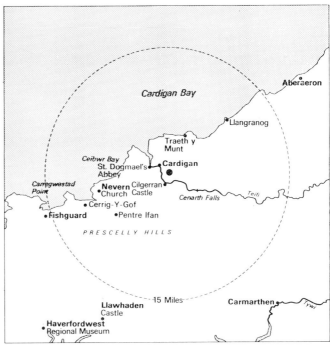

strayed outside a five mile radius from the house. Super walks and we managed to wangle a go in a coracle one evening".

"Very nice indeed, just sit and listen".

15

The College

Week St. Mary, Cornwall

ONE OF OUR VISITORS told us that this building was for sale and sent us a snapshot of it. We were attracted by the elaborate doorway of granite, reminiscent of that at Wortham Manor (p. 155), and on inspection it was clear that here was part only of something that had been much larger; there were carved fragments in the walls of neighbouring houses and early Tudor windows in the sheds attached to the building. It turns out that these are the remains of a remarkable school, almost the first to be founded by a woman—Lady Berkeley's at Wotton-under-Edge, and that of Margaret Tudor, Henry VIII's grandmother, at Wimborne, being the only earlier ones.

Moreover the woman who founded it, Thomasine Bonaventure, was herself very remarkable. Though born obscurely here, she married a London merchant, who died leaving her his property. She then married another City merchant who also died leaving her his property. Her third husband was Lord Mayor of London; when he died, leaving her much of his property, she gave or bequeathed everything to charity, amongst many other benefactions founding in 1506 this school at the place of her birth.

The College does, it emerges, have a connection with Wortham, which is only twelve miles away. Thomasine appointed her first cousin, John Dinham to supervise the building work; he built the porch at Wortham, and this is doubtless why the doorways of the two houses resemble each other.

Unfortunately she laid it down that the master (who was to have an Oxford or a Cambridge degree, and six weeks holiday a year) should pray for the souls of her husbands; and consequently, although the school was said in 1546 to be "a great comfort to all the country there, for they that list may set their children to board there and have them taught freely", nevertheless it was, as a chantry, dissolved two years later, and its endowment transferred to the school at Launceston.

Thus the College at Week St. Mary, one of the oldest of English schools, prosperously founded, which might with reasonable luck have grown into a public school, survives only in its name which, remarkably, still clings to this house more than four hundred years later.

How is all this known? Mr. Hawker, the Vicar of Morwenstow, had written an account of Thomasine, more romantic than accurate, in his "Footprints of former men in far Cornwall"; but in 1972 a large illuminated manuscript, of obscure provenance, was sold at Sotheby's. The buyer wished it to go to the United States, and therefore it had to come before the Reviewing Committee on the Export of Works of Art—who refused to let it go. This was Thomasine's original deed founding the school, now in the Cornwall County Record Office, where it has prompted a most scholarly study of the college by Mr. P. L. Hull.

There is a curious parallel here with the story of another Cornish building, twelve miles away. About twenty-five years ago an application was made to this same Reviewing Committee for permission to export some panelling and other fittings. An architect was sent to inspect—and thus were discovered at Dunsland House, now alas destroyed by fire, unaltered interiors of the 1660's of the very highest quality. The house outside was just a box of ivy,

and inside it had not even been redecorated; I remember the panelling grained to resemble walnut with big yellow acanthus leaves painted over the cornices; locks, grates, plaster work, all of the best, all untouched. The explanation of such excellence in so unexpected a spot proved to be that when, at the restoration, Charles II provided workmen to build grand houses in north Cornwall for Monk and for Grenville (at Stowe—see p. 95), both of whom had greatly helped him, they in turn lent these workmen to the owner of Dunsland, who happened to be a first cousin of each of them.

The College faces a little courtyard off the village street. Behind it a meadow slopes down to a chequerwork of small fields; and over them appears, black and afar, the high outline of Dartmoor, beyond which Thomasine ventured to such purpose.

Coombe

Nr. Morwenstow, Bude, North Cornwall

COOMBE, SIX MILES NORTH OF BUDE, consists of a watermill, the millhouse, and several cottages built round a ford on a shallow, fast-running stream. It is at the junction of two wooded valleys and is half a mile from the sea at Duckpool, where a sandy beach is exposed at half tide.

Although a small and humble place, Coombe has greatness behind it, since it is where the Grenville family came from. They owned Coombe and lived at Stowe Barton a few hundred yards up the hill. Having, with Monk, been the prime movers in the restoration of Charles II, they then became a good deal richer and more

important; Stowe Barton was rebuilt, and substantial and interesting traces remain of the house and surroundings.

Coombe is also in the parish of Morwenstow, whose famous vicar, the Rev. Stephen Hawker, lived at Coombe for a short time. He was the inventor (or perhaps reviver) of harvest festivals, and a moving spirit in the saving of life at sea— and, if it could not be saved on this difficult coast, of providing Christian burial for the drowned. The Reverend Sabine Baring-Gould (author of "Onward Christian Soldiers") wrote a life of Hawker. This book, by one famous and unusual parson about another, sheds an unexpected light on the Victorians, and we have managed to get enough copies to put one in most of the cottages at Coombe.

The Landmark Trust acquired Coombe—buildings, gardens and orchards—as part of a joint scheme with the National Trust to preserve it and its exceptional setting. It is a sheltered place, lying back from the sea, which our forefathers sensibly preferred to living on the coast itself. Almost all the surrounding land, including much of the coast, now belongs to the National Trust, ourselves or the Forestry Commission, and we have done a great deal of work clearing away old sheds, etc., and putting electricity and telephone wires as far as possible underground. There are long and excellent walks along the coast (geologically one of the most impressive in Britain), and in all other directions. From the logbooks, there is clearly much wild life, including trout in the stream. One visitor tickled and ate

nine. The Mill itself, in working order though not in use, is a handsome and interesting stone building with a fine millwheel.

The Carpenter's Shop

Coombe
The Mill House

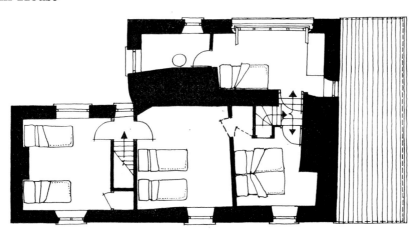

FIRST FLOOR
NO. 1.

FIRST FLOOR
NO. 2.

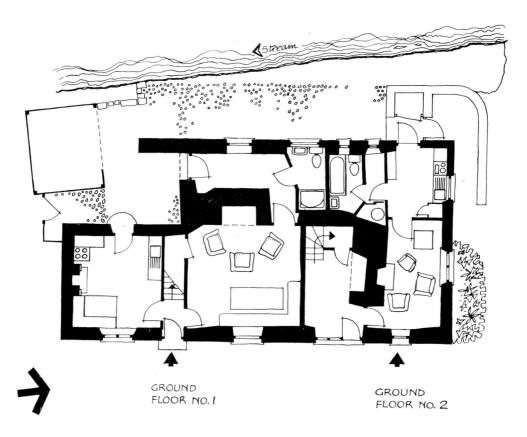

GROUND
FLOOR NO. 1

GROUND
FLOOR NO. 2

20

Coombe
The Mill House

This is built of stone and cob with a thatched and slated roof, and is divided into two. The stream runs past a cobbled terrace at the back. One bedroom in each part of the house looks down the valley towards the sea.

From the logbook (No. 1)

"The stream is really good . . . Charlotte my sister's glasses got carried away by the current . . . Plenty of gumboots and trousers are needed, in fact mostly shorts . . . We followed the stream down to the sea, which was lovely . . ."

"We managed to add Nuthatch to the list of birds seen and two mink were reported by the bridge".

"I walked to Hartland Point (very tiring—hitched back), my wife read the books on Geology and our 14 month old son enjoyed seeing the stream almost come over into the kitchen. Our second visit—and not the last we hope".

"The path up through the wood towards Stowe is probably an old pack-horse route".

"By 2 p.m. the stream had risen 18 inches and was a rich brown torrent smelling of soil. By nightfall the largest stone viewed from the back door had surfaced again for the benefit of the grey wagtails".

"Many photographs were taken to keep memories alive".

"Driven by a single-minded eleven year old with a tape recorder we set out one evening after supper to record the otters".

"Stoke Church—don't forget to climb

Coombe

The Mill House

the tower, highest in Devon, always unlocked".

"Once again found the library extremely interesting—really looked forward to my evening in the armchair reading".

"The only sounds have been the sea, the stream, the wind, and children enjoying themselves, with intermittent bird song".

From the logbook (No. 2)

"Every day we went for some sort of walk: we never used the car except for the week's shopping".

"We liked St. Juliot church. This is the one that Thomas Hardy was working on as architect while he wooed the Rector's sister-in-law and wrote 'A Pair of Blue Eyes'. It was satisfying to note that the restoration was not all that well done, proving that you can't do three things at once".

"The eels like cheese, bacon rind and hard boiled eggs".

"Try going up to Morwenstow Church late in the afternoon, and just sit in one of the pews".

"At Tintagel we liked 'King Arthur's Car Park' and the Excali-Bar—definitely a tour-de-farce".

"I've done so little, I am glad to say".

Ford Cottage

This is an extremely old cottage of cob and thatch on the edge of the stream, close to the Mill House. It has a large high living-room with a slate floor and an open fire which works. There is a large orchard at the back, running alongside the stream.

Coombe

Ford Cottage

From the logbook

"Although there is nothing terrifically exciting to do, the surrounding countryside has kept us all occupied".

"Duckpool is a wild and rocky cove—big thundering waves and enough sand for thousands of castles".

"We were a party of 17, taking the Mill House, Hawker's, Chapel and Ford . . . In the evening, with log fires burning brightly, parties gathered in invited cottages. Bridge, backgammon, chat and fudge flowed freely".

"The young man who is the potter at Welcombe has a marvellous old Austin Ruby in his garage".

"Nice one, Landmark".

"It is recorded that Purcell played on the organ in Kilkhampton church".

"Another enjoyable day was spent following the Bude canal. We walked from the lock in Bude along the towpath to the inclined plane at Marhamchurch".

"Christmas morning was very beautiful".

"The great fairground organ at the Devon Museum of Mechanical Music has an output which can only be compared with '1812' in the Albert Hall".

"We have done very little: It seemed a pity to leave the cottage and its wonderfully peaceful surroundings".

"Several areas of sound well-jointed rock are tempting to the climber".

"In November the local people have time to talk. Perhaps they're just polite, but they have been kind to us".

"If only we could transport some of this tranquillity to where we live".

"Dare one say it? Ford Cottage in January is enthusiastically recommended".

"We treasure the thought that our experience will be shared by those who follow us here in the years to come".

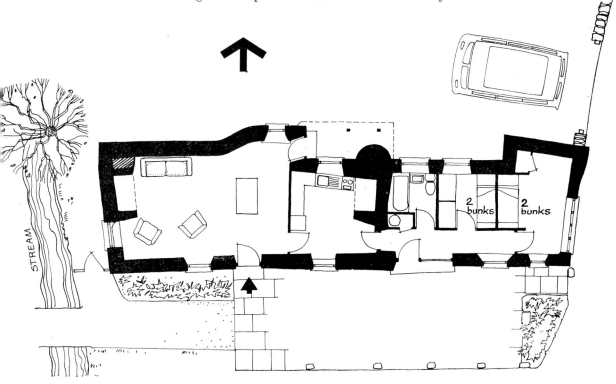

Coombe

No. 2 Hawker's Cottages

This is one of a pair of stone, cob, and thatched cottages, called after the famous Vicar of Morwenstow who lived here briefly. It has a large and handsome living-room with a polished slate floor and a particularly splendid old cupboard. There is also a small sitting-room; so that in this Landmark at least the quiet and the noisy can be separated. The garden in front of the house is small, sheltered and very pretty. Next door, at no. 1, lives our warden.

From the logbook

"The children did not wish to return home".

"The motte and bailey near Kilkhampton will always be remembered because that is where we saw the badger in the moat on a sunny Saturday afternoon. We watched it snuffling along for ages—and I took a photo to prove it".

"Just the sound of wind and rain and a crackling fire".

"If this is your first visit to this part of the world, you will probably want to go out on motor drives to explore the surrounding area. The temptation should be resisted. The best spots are here, in the garden and around the Mill stream and in the valley generally".

"Drepanaspis remains at Watergate Bay".

"We had a memorable day going to Boscastle, Crackington and Beeny High Cliff and walking out to Cambeak in a quite tremendous wind. The same wild wind was whipping up the sea as we sat in Hawker's Hut and watched the rain storms coming in from the horizon".

Coombe
No. 2 Hawker's Cottages

"At night we caught three different kinds of toad".

"Canadian born and of Icelandic heritage I know I am only one of thousands of visitors to this lovely land who feel a great sense of gratitude to those responsible for keeping by much planning and restoration these matchless little homes and surroundings".

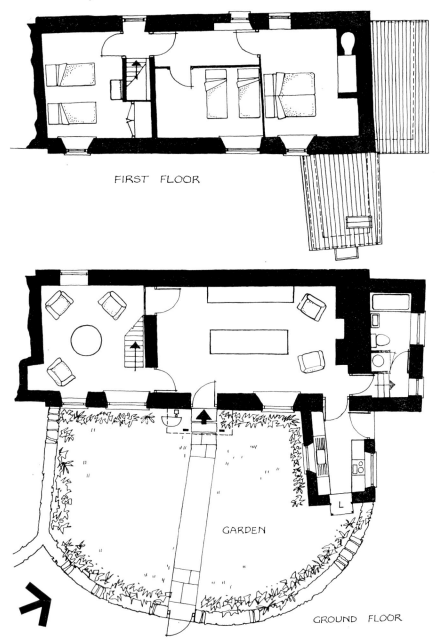

FIRST FLOOR

GARDEN

GROUND FLOOR

Coombe
The Carpenter's Shop

This was originally the estate workshop. Until recently derelict, we have replaced the corrugated iron roof with the original slates. It is a handsome stone building with a spare, functional interior—a large living-room open to the roof and two double bedrooms upstairs leading off the gallery, reached by a spiral stair. The living-room has a slate floor and an open fire, formerly the forge. Outside there is a large old orchard leading down to the stream.

From the logbook

"The house is delightful down to the tea-cups, and wet days pass pleasantly on that account".

"The weather for the early time of year has been days of blue skies and meals under the apple trees in the orchard".

"There is no need to go anywhere".

"The power of the Atlantic waves against the contorted strata of the rock face is astounding. Note the overthrusting and faulting, the acute synclines and anticlines. Couldn't find the one-inch bands of coal, but they are there".

"It must be impossible to be unhappy here".

"We were greatly honoured by meeting some of the workmen who had restored the Carpenter's Shop".

"The week has been one of the nicest any of us has ever spent anywhere".

"The jigsaw proceeded slowly aided by readings aloud from 'The Vicar of Morwenstow'".

"Some of the rarest flowers are within a few yards of Carpenter's, e.g. Pyrenean lilies on the bank in the lane".

Coombe
The Carpenter's Shop

". . . the children creeping out of their beds to look over the gallery, tempted by laughter and the tinkle of glasses below".

"We wish all who come here happiness and peace. We certainly found this charming house a haven of rest".

"We found a seagull's feather with which I have written this account of our short but very pleasant stay".

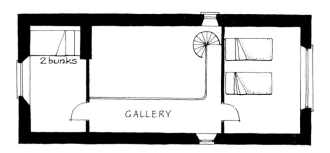

FIRST FLOOR

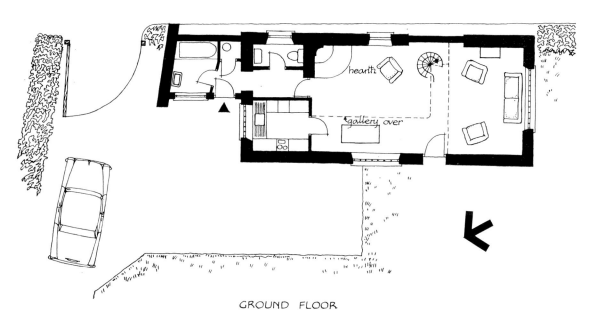

GROUND FLOOR

Coombe
Chapel Cottage

This is a handsome nineteenth-century mission room, of slate and weather-board with sash windows. It had been rather brutally added to and altered over the years, but we have restored the mission room itself (for some reason, perhaps fiscal, originally built on wheels still visible under the front) and we have improved the appearance, and interior, of the addition.

It is very well placed—a little above the rest of Coombe, looking across the valley over the top of one of the orchards.

From the logbook

"For those who may be interested in antiquity there is within 2½ miles of here a fine example of a motte and bailey, one of the best I have seen ... To reach it makes a good walk; start on the path through the wood behind the mill house ...".

"Sandymouth Cove has enormous rocks showing variable colours and strata".

"Chapel Cottage at Christmas; everything one could desire—quiet, frosty, but good walking weather, returning with appetites high. Two herons near the stream, a magnificent pair indeed".

"We have spent a blissful 3 days doing absolutely nothing".

"We visited Morwenstow when a great wind was blowing from the S.W.—sky overcast, sea slate green, the gale scraping the cliffs. We deemed the rude home-made hut of the Rev. Hawker much more impressive than the ruins at Tintagel".

"We stayed here for a long weekend. It was very pleasant as it always is".

"The children much enjoyed the piano".

Coombe
Chapel Cottage

"Thoroughly recommend Sunday tea at the satellite tracking station—charming American hosts".

"A lovely peaceful place, as all the Landmark houses are".

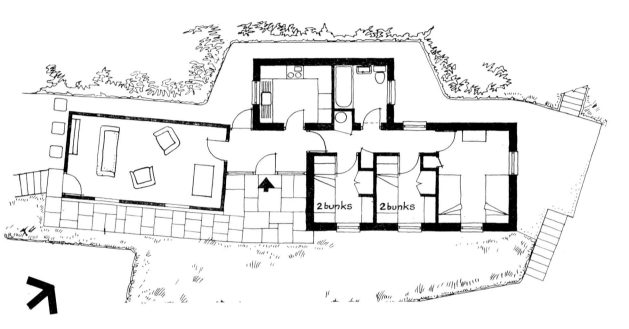

Coombe Mill

Clytha Castle
Near Abergavenny, Gwent

"ERECTED IN THE YEAR 1790 by William Jones of Clytha House, husband of Elizabeth, last surviving child of Sir William Morgan of Tredegar, it was undertaken with the purpose of relieving a mind afflicted by the loss of a most excellent wife, to the memory of whose virtues this tablet is dedicated".

At the suggestion of the National Trust, we have taken a long lease of this folly which stands on the summit of a small hill, at the edge of a grove of old chestnuts. It has the air of a place that has been both loved and neglected. The square tower contains fine rooms on both floors.

We have repaired the whole building and so, we hope, have enabled it once again to relieve the minds of those who frequent it.

From the logbook

"Three buzzards soared over the castle for ten minutes this morning."

"Coming from Australia we weren't worried by noises, etc. in the night".

"The children bought a cheap pillow-case (15p) at Abergavenny market and out of this made a flag. The pole is still up on the battlements for future occupants to use".

"The views from the towpath of the canal west of Gilwern were magnificent".

"We would simply like to record the passing of a beautiful and peaceful week-end—with much feasting—at this lovely place".

"Usk is a pleasant town with a proper baker".

"Whilst sitting on the battlements, we were surprised to see a hot air balloon floating towards us".

"The acoustics in the sitting room are excellent".

Clytha Castle

"Our intentions were to dine out every night, but the atmosphere of the dining room was too much to resist".

"All the three children can now swim".

"Clytha is well up to Landmark's own high standards; it's the ninth we've been to, so we ought to know".

"We have enjoyed awakening to the cawing of the rooks and going to sleep listening to the owls calling".

"The 800 piece jigsaw was completed this evening just in time".

"We hope that Clytha castle rewards you with the same peace of mind that it afforded us, and thank the Landmark Trust for giving us such happiness".

31

Clytha Castle

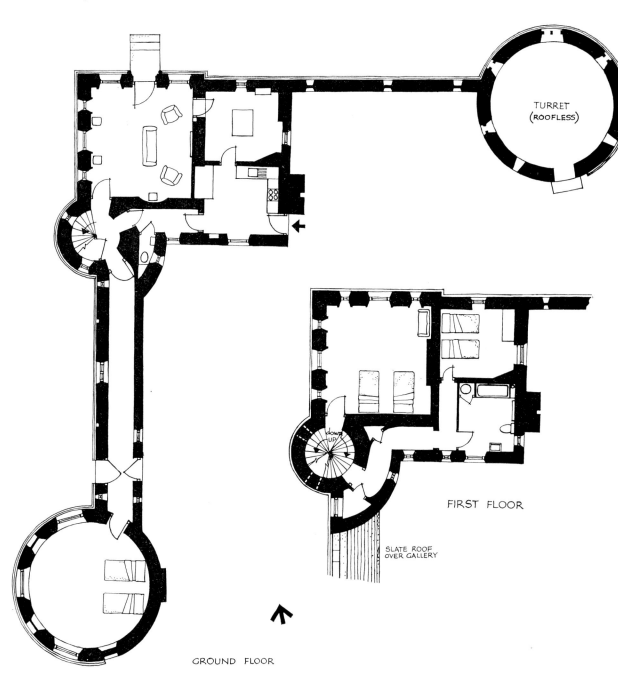

TURRET
(ROOFLESS)

FIRST FLOOR

SLATE ROOF
OVER GALLERY

GROUND FLOOR

Edale Mill
Derbyshire

THIS COTTON MILL was built in the late eighteenth century, and during the whole of its long working life has survived the hazards of finance and fire, to both of which such mills were prone. In the nineteenth century it was extended at each end and the stone staircase tower was added. When the Manchester to Sheffield railway was built through the Hope valley in the 1890's it became practicable to use coal; the water wheel was removed and the mill was powered by steam until its then owners, Fine Spinners and Doublers Ltd., closed it in 1934.

We bought it in 1969, removed the slate roof, reinstated sash windows, and divided the interior into seven dwellings—one of which we have kept as a Landmark. Our architect, Mr. George Robb, took particular trouble with such details as the gutters and downpipes—the latter

being specially made for us square in section, which makes all the difference to the mill's appearance; and we have put the telephone and electricity underground. In spite of these apparent extravagances the whole project turned out to be perfectly economic and the mill, instead of being demolished as it would have been, will now, I hope, remain an ornament to the dale and a monument to those who laboured in it.

From the logbook

"We arrived and departed by train and this is to be recommended—particularly to arrive by walking down the road from the station to savour something of the mill's situation".

Edale Mill

Edale Mill

"The right combination of luxury and puritanism".

"A visit to the Nag's Head makes a splendid evening walk across the fields along the footpath opposite Skinners Hall".

"Today we got up at 6.30 a.m. to walk over to Castleton in time to catch a bus, and then another bus to Bakewell—from there to Haddon Hall . . ."

"You do recover from a twenty mile walk".

"We went for a long walk, twelve miles or so, through Edale village, up the stream to the moor and along it Eastwards to the Roman track . . . hot sunshine and no wind all day long. Many grouse close enough to see clearly"

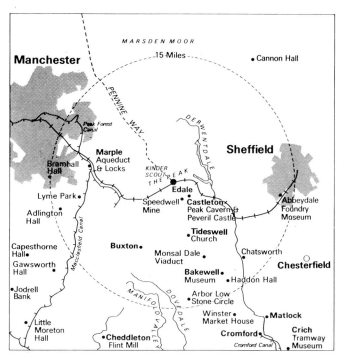

"A-level geographical field work. Five days hard and rewarding work, getting the most out of this part of Britain. We worked till 7 p.m. on average, and conversations kept getting geographical even after that in the pub".

"The days were bright and clear and the nights freezing—I've never seen so many stars".

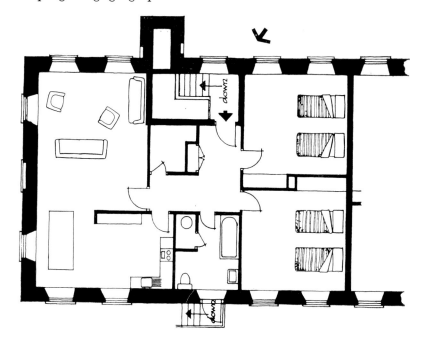

35

The Danescombe Mine
Calstock, Cornwall

THESE ARE THE monumental buildings of the old Cotehele Consols copper and arsenic mine. They are unusually well built, handsome, and complete, and stand by a stream in a steep wooded valley leading down to the Tamar. We have taken a long lease of them from the National Trust and have consolidated and repaired them, so that it is now possible to stay here, in comfort but not luxury, and study at close quarters the tremendous past of the Devon and Cornish mines. It was a romantic but dreadful trade which enriched amongst others the Dukes of Bedford and the father of William Morris.

The engine house, which we have made habitable, is strongly built of the Killas stone in which the lodes occur, and contained a rotary beam engine with a forty inch cylinder driving a Taylor roll

crusher, a pump, and two buddles on the dressing floor. The mine worked, on and off, from 1822 to 1900, kept alive at the last by the demand for arsenic to dress cotton against the boll weevil. In the woods above lie abandoned shafts of the Wheal Calstock and Consolidated Tamar mines, and of earlier mines still.

It is a short and beautiful walk through the woods above the Tamar to Cotehele, a most notable medieval house for centuries the home of the Edgcumbes and now opened by the National Trust. Few Landmarks have more to offer than Danescombe.

From the logbook
"Take an illicit stroll over Calstock viaduct after the last train has gone".

The Danescombe Mine

"There is an adit on the Marquis Lode of the Bedford United mine above Gunnislake that shows some of the original timbering".

"The farmer is a nice person and it is interesting, my brother says, to see how they put the tops of the milk on the bottles".

"The mine shafts at the rear contain pipestrelle bats".

"Who else could have made an arsenic mine so inviting?"

Before

The Danescombe Mine

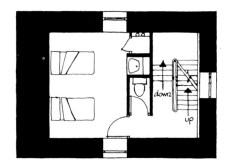

FIRST FLOOR

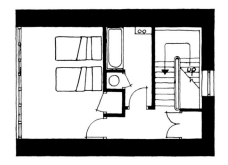

SECOND FLOOR

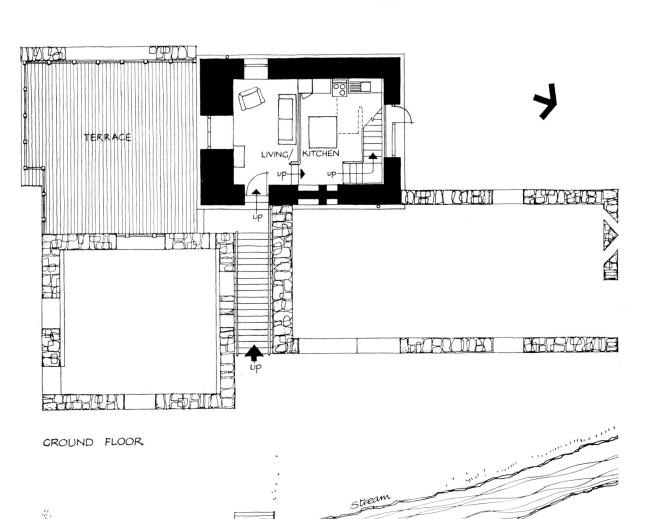

GROUND FLOOR

The Egyptian House
Chapel St., Penzance, Cornwall

WITH THE EXCEPTION of an Egyptian factory in Leeds, and Foulston's mutilated library at Devonport, this is the only remaining building in a style which enjoyed a vogue after Napoleon's campaign in Egypt of 1798. The front elevation is almost identical with that of the former Egyptian Hall in Piccadilly, designed in 1812 by P. F. Robinson. Since he also designed Trelissick House near Truro (fine surroundings, worth a visit) Robinson may well have been the architect of the Egyptian House.

It was built at the higher end of Chapel Street for Mr George Lavin as a museum and geological repository. Behind its colossal facade with lotus bud capitals and enrichments of Coade stone (that wonderful material of still unknown composition) lay, when we bought it in 1968, two small granite houses above shops, solid, and with a pleasant rear elevation, but very decrepit inside. These, in the course of our work to the front, we have reconstructed as three flats, the highest of which has a fine view of Mounts Bay and St. Michael's Mount across the chimney pots of Chapel Street.

Why was there a geological shop here in the early nineteenth century? Although picked over by the Victorians (doubtless including Mr Lavin) the beaches at Penzance hold every kind of pebble, deposited by long-vanished glaciers. Just listen to this: "The pebble-collector should linger on the Marazion and Penzance beaches as long as possible, for here he should find many choice specimens for his cabinet. Pebbles of porphyritic granite, quartz, quartzite, quartz-veined slate, greenstone, serpentine, jasper in various shades, agate, chalcedony, citrine, carnelian and amethystine quartz, together with fossiliferous flints await his discerning scrutiny. The pebbles of these and neighbouring beaches on the Cornish coast are remarkable, not only for their lustrous beauty when cut and polished, but also for the extent of their geological range".

Penzance, still accessible by train, is a handsome and agreeable town, good for walks and buying fish; and beyond it lies that hard old peninsula in which, at places like Chysauster and the Botallack mine, can be found moving evidences of human labour, separated by an immense span of time.

From the logbook

"An oval staircase, a sofa with curved ends, and a window seat, three of the most important things in my house of dreams, how surprised and pleased I was to find them in a holiday flat".

"Perfect place to be when writing a book as I was".

"Penzance is worth exploring, far more so than the prettified St. Ives".

"I liked the window seat because you can at night see the lighthouse flashing off and on".

"Do note the telephone box at junction of B3315 and B3283—impeccably attended to, complete with fresh flowers, carpet and ash tray, and daily sprayed with aerosol".

"On Sunday morning you can take a boat from Penzance Harbour to St. Michael's Mount for the service in the chapel".

"A lovely flat which has been home for the past two weeks".

"The most enjoyable part of our holiday was an evening walk along the front at Penzance to Newlyn harbour to watch the fishing boats come in. Then fish and chips (still wrapped in the Radio Times) and a walk back".

"What an initiation into the pleasures of the Landmark Trust".

The Egyptian House

"On the coast path you go by many tin and copper mines which make a pretty sight standing out like soldiers on the hills".

"We much appreciated the furniture and delighted in the witty Egyptian motifs".

"The Mechanical Music Museum at Goldsithney runs a Thursday night concert of classical music on their automatic pianos".

"The top floor has been a very comfortable home for the past week. We lacked nothing and enjoyed the views from all the windows".

"The cinema at Helston has attractive features; the built-in ice cream stall beside the screen and the framed picture [of B. Bardot *circa* 1960 to name but two."

"I was glad I also spent time looking closely at the rood screen in St. Buryan Church, and in finding that most peculiar place, Gwennap Pit".

"If you are here at Christmas, don't miss the illumination at Mousehole, featuring the Loch Ness Monster".

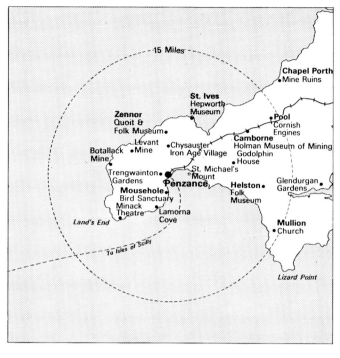

"Train to St. Ives is beautiful, it goes round the coast: come back by bus, also very beautiful".

". . . windows with views of St. Michael's Mount, a lighthouse, a church clock with a flat chime, seagulls seen through the skylights, an elliptical staircase, exquisite furniture, and a barrel organ in the street".

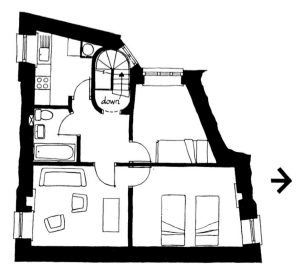

FLOOR PLAN

Fort Clonque
Alderney, Channel Islands

IN THE EIGHTEEN-FORTIES it was thought that the advent of steam would make the Channel Islands more important as an advanced naval base, and also more liable to capture by the French. Accordingly "with the strong support of Sir J. Burgoyne and the Duke of Wellington" the great harbour works of Alderney were begun in 1842. Fort Clonque, the most remarkable of the defences built to protect this harbour, occupies a group of large rocks about 300 yards off the steep and uninhabited south-west tip of Alderney, commanding the passage between Alderney and the island of Burhou. It is reached by a causeway and was originally designed for ten 64-pounder guns in four open batteries, manned by two officers and fifty men.

Very soon however the further development of steam brought the Channel Islands within a few hours of Portland,

Plymouth or Portsmouth, and made a fourth base in Alderney unnecessary — while the development of naval gunnery made these granite forts, with their moats, drawbridges and loop-holes, seem old fashioned and insecure. In 1886, when Alderney was still defended by 222 eight- and ten-inch guns, the Defence Committee recommended that Clonque and all the other works except Fort Albert should be disarmed, but left standing.

It was in this condition that Hitler found them in 1940 when, making the same mistake that we had made a hundred years before in imagining that the Channel Islands would have strategic value, he vigorously refortified them. At Fort Clonque part of the Victorian soldiers' quarters was demolished and replaced by an enormous casemate, housing a gun so large that its emplacement now makes a handsome sitting room looking towards

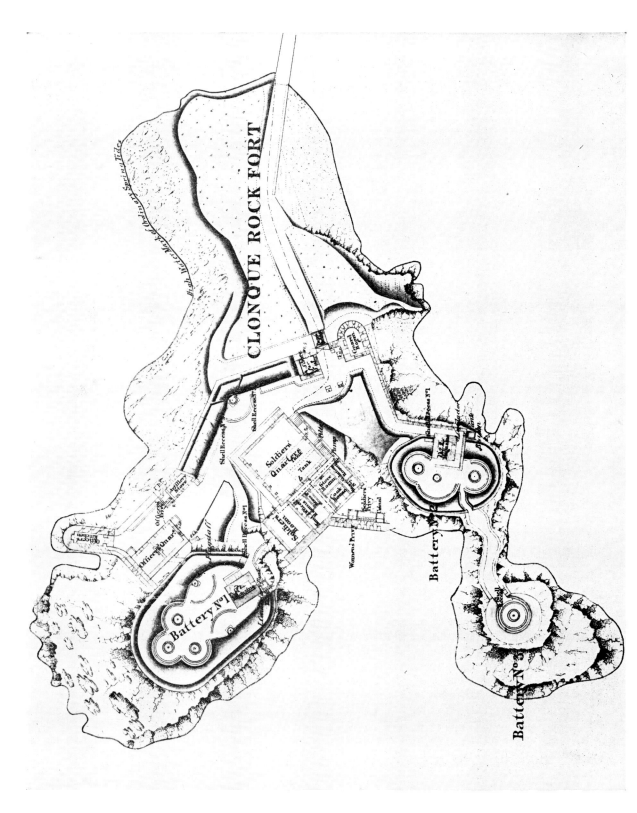

CLONQUE ROCK FORT

Battery Nº1

Battery Nº2

Battery Nº3

Fort Clonque

Guernsey, with a ceiling eleven feet thick. This casemate is monumental in scale and an addition to the history of Clonque; but elsewhere in the fort the Germans did lamentable damage which it has taken us years to repair. Almost all the work, much of it very heavy and difficult, has been done by Mr. A. W. Markell, the retired superintendent of the Admiralty breakwater, a man of the highest standards.

Most forts are of necessity large and grim, but Clonque, because it is small and because it has had to be fitted to the great rocks round which it is built, is open and picturesque, ingeniously contrived on many levels with stretches of grass here and there. Samphire and mesembryanthemum have

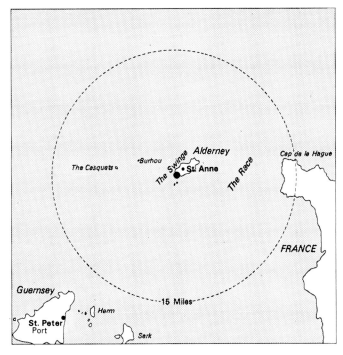

spread, and the clean air allows all sorts of lichen to grow on the granite walls, whose solidity and texture are a constant pleasure to the eye at every angle of the sun. On calm days the sea can be heard all round, restlessly searching the rocks; and on rough days it is comforting to reflect that the wall of the East Flank Battery is nineteen feet thick. At extreme low tide a reef is exposed to the South West, and one can clamber far out along it, peering into the depths. At high tide the fort is cut off and the sea runs between it and the mainland, releasing its phosphorence as it passes over the submerged causeway. All the time there is a marine view second to none — of the other islands, rocks and stacks; of the two great colonies of gannets, which fish round the fort; of the lighthouses on the Cas-

quets; of the big ships which move along the horizon; and of the formidable race or current called the Swinge which runs between Clonque and Burhou. On all counts, Fort Clonque is one of the most worthwhile places we have tackled, not least because when we embarked on it in 1966 military works such as this were disregarded everywhere.

The rest of Alderney is also extremely pleasant; the island is just small enough to be explored entirely on foot or, very easily, by bicycle; all the Victorian and German defence works are interesting; the beaches at the North end are exceptional; and in the centre is St. Anne, a very pretty little town, greatly expanded for the garrison in a plain classical style, English with a hint of France.

Hole Cottage
Cowden, Nr. Edenbridge, Kent

THIS IS THE surviving cross-wing of a late medieval timber-framed hall-house. It lies by a small stream in a woodland clearing accessible, just, by car; but, curiously enough, most accessible by railway, since it is only a ten minute walk through the wood from Cowden Station — until recently lit by oil lamps which the porter extinguished when the last train had gone, but now alas electrified.

The Hole has very much the true feeling of the Weald, and of the deep woods in whose drip and shade the forges and furnaces of the Sussex ironmasters were established. It is a quiet solitary place where you may enjoy a sleepy fire, the smell of smoke, the huge shadows of trees, and the sound of the stream.

From the logbook

"We arrived late by train: the stationmaster guided us through the trees".

"We didn't go anywhere as it is so nice here".

"It's all green, and suddenly the cottage is standing there as it has been all the time".

"Milk awaited us in the fridge, but no matter how many notes with money we left, in bottles, tins or under stones etc,. we never succeeded in getting any more".

"Chiddingstone Castle is just a country house with knobs on".

"The landlord of the Kentish Horse has

Hole Cottage

a good strong cider, which he is reluctant to serve to ladies in large quantities".

"Please keep quiet about this place at all costs".

"If you go to see Hever Castle, be sure to take plenty of money".

"Thank you Hole Cottage".

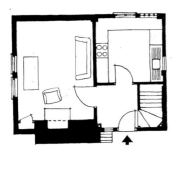

GROUND FLOOR

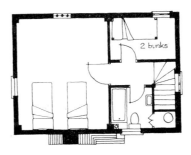

FIRST FLOOR

34 High Street
Ironbridge, Shropshire

THE SALE PARTICULARS SAID: "These premises have been occupied by the Firm of Messrs. Egerton Smith & Sons for many years. These were specially built, at a great cost, by the late Mr. Smith, and occupy a Unique Position in Ironbridge". They certainly do—unique indeed in the world, overlooking that harbinger of our age, forerunner and survivor, the Iron Bridge.

The market place, on the river side of which no. 34 stands, was laid out as a direct consequence of the building of the bridge in 1779. An open air market is still held here on Fridays. No. 34 was the complete establishment of a substantial grocer, with a large house over a double-fronted shop; three floors of store rooms with trap doors in each floor and the original crane still in the roof; an office, stables, coach house, cart house, 'bacon drying house'; and two cellars, one under the other, the lower one communicating by a tunnel with the bank of the River Severn, up which, until the late nineteenth century, cargoes were brought by barge.

We have let the shop to the Ironbridge Gorge Museum Trust, and in it they sell books and other things irresistible to anyone interested at all in industrial history. Mr. Smith's quarters upstairs we have divided into two, one part let to a permanent tenant, and the other part, on two floors, for visitors. The living room has a particularly fine iron fireplace cast here in Coalbrookdale, (as was the bathroom basin and the lavatory cistern), and

34 High Street

Before

After

Within

34 High Street

this and every other room faces the river, the bridge, and the steep woods beyond. It is a wonderful place to be, with the sun glittering on the rather muddy Severn as it flows inexhaustibly beneath Abraham Darby's iron arch —and all around, in Coalport, Ironbridge, and Coalbrookdale, remains of industry's beginning.

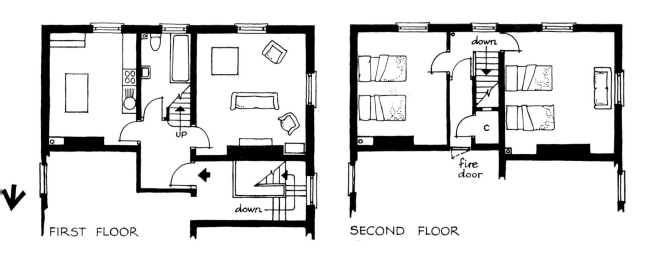

FIRST FLOOR

SECOND FLOOR

NORTH
LIGHT

*Old Copper
Mine*

ATLANTIC

OCEAN

Brazen Ward

THREEQUARTER WALL

TIBBETTS

Jenny's Cove

HALFWAY WALL

LUNDY

ROADS

*Battery
Point*

QUARTER WALL

OLD LIGHT

THE
BARN

MILLCOMBE
HOUSE

THE OLD
SCHOOL

ST JOHNS

HANMERS

*Landing
Beach*

SIGNAL
COTTAGE

CASTLE

*Rat
Island*

SOUTH
LIGHT

Shutter Point

Great Shutter Rock

0   1 MILE

Lundy
via Ilfracombe, North Devon

THE ISLAND OF LUNDY, in the approaches to the Bristol Channel, is just over three miles long by about half a mile wide and stands over four hundred feet out of the sea, commanding a tremendous view of England, Wales and the Atlantic. It has tall granite cliffs towards the West, and sloping but steep sidelands, with trees and vegetation in small hanging valleys, on the more sheltered East coast facing the mainland. There are three lighthouses (two in use), a castle, a church, a farm, no traffic, and a population of about twenty five concentrated at the South end of the island. Most of the buildings, and all the field walls, are made of the island's light-coloured granite.

Lundy offers both the pleasures of escape and the pleasures of participation. Field studies (archaeology, birds, botany, etc.), diving and rockclimbing draw some people to Lundy, but doing nothing here is also very rewarding; and, for everybody, the sea and space, the silence, the life of the island and the natural world make a stay a rare experience. So

tranquil, solid and unaffected a place has a remarkable power to refresh the spirits of its visitors.

The island is not always easy to reach, or to leave, and you have to land on the open beach. To want to go there, and to do it, needs a trace of enterprise. A visit is a small adventure, especially if you travel in our cargo ship, the Polar Bear, built for service on the west coast of Greenland. Lundy, though tame indeed by the standards of the great explorers, does offer to all who have accompanied them in spirit a minor prospect of a far horizon.

When in 1969 the island was advertised for sale by auction, the National Trust considered buying it, but decided that it could not do so. We therefore offered to underwrite an appeal to raise the purchase price, and then to restore and run the island if the National Trust would accept ownership. This appeal, sponsored by Mr. Jeremy Thorpe, Mr. Peter Mills, and Dr. David Owen, was successful, thanks largely to Mr. Jack Hayward, and since

Lundy

1969 we have been gradually rehabilitating the island's buildings and services. We recognise that slow decline is probably the most agreeable and natural state of affairs for a small island, but decline, if it is to continue, has to be reversed occasionally.

Owing to its distance from the mainland, Lundy will always be expensive to run; therefore we make it possible to stay on the island at various levels of price and comfort — small hotel, cottages, hostel, camping — so that almost anyone can afford to be here, though Lundy's resources limit the total number. Everyone has the free run of the whole island at all times.

To know more about Lundy, write to us for the Lundy guide; and, if this handbook has lost its copy, write to us also for the leaflet "Staying on Lundy", which greatly amplifies the brief details given below.

Millcombe House, built about 1835 by the Heaven family in a plain classical style, is now used by us as a small hotel (12 beds, 3 baths). Its well-proportioned rooms contain some very agreeable old furniture and pictures. The curious inward-sloping copper roof, which we have restored to its original form, was designed to catch rainwater.

Lundy

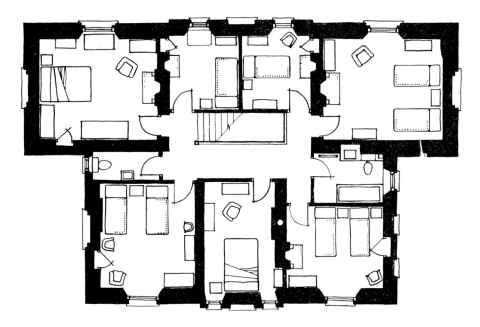

FIRST FLOOR

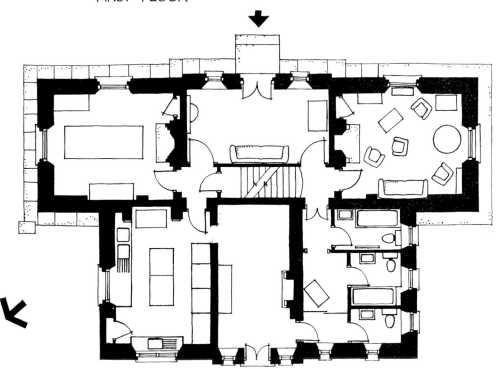

GROUND FLOOR

Climbing the Devil's Slide

Mr. Michael Haycraft pointing the Castle

Signal Cottages are a pair, built in 1885 for the staff of the telegraph station. They do not make a distinguished build-ing, but they have a fine view past the South Light to the coast of Devon.

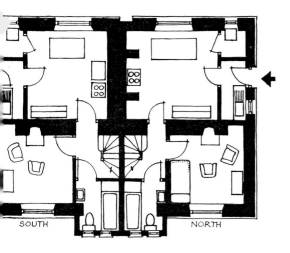 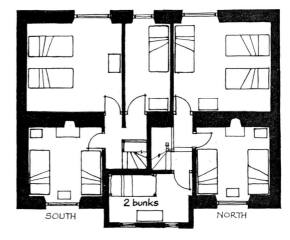

GROUND FLOOR · FIRST FLOOR

Castle cottage is a single-storey granite addition to the keep of the castle, built originally for the cable station and later enlarged. It has a view over the South Light better even than that of Signal Cottages.

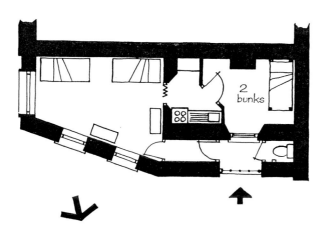

Lundy

Hanmers was built by a fisherman in 1902 (for £150). He chose a good site, a dip in the hill, on the path from the beach to the castle, so that the place is sheltered but has a wonderful view. It has a very pleasant wood-lined interior.

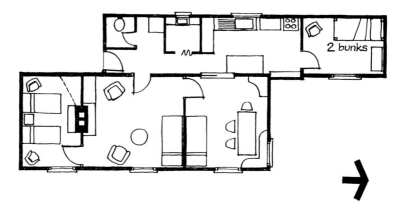

Big and Little St. John's are a pair of modern single-storey cottages built by the Harman family on either side of an existing granite structure, looking South-East across the St. John's valley and out to sea.

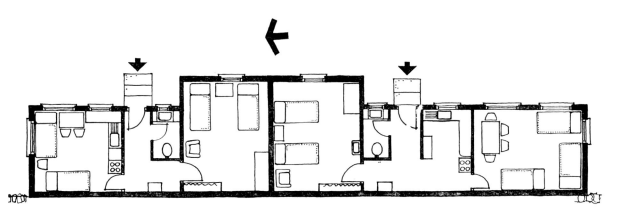

The Old School, known as "the blue bung", shares the same outlook as the St. John's cottages. It is a small building of corrugated iron, lined with matchboard-ing—but, in spite of this rather lowering description, it has considerable point and charm.

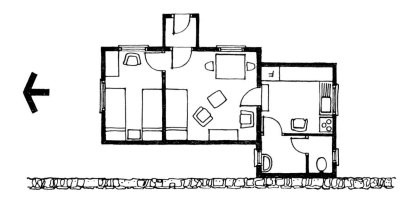

Lundy

Tibbetts is a beautifully designed and constructed granite building, put up as an Admiralty lookout in 1909, on the second highest point of the island. It is about 1¾ miles along the main North-South track, and is remote and windy even by Lundy standards. From it fourteen lighthouses can be seen on a clear night. The interior is lined with varnished matchboarding and keeps its original purposeful atmosphere

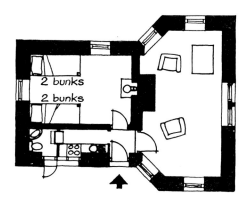

Lundy

The Barn, which was roofless when we arrived, is a granite building with a round-house attached, and is at the centre of island life. We have turned it into a more than ordinarily comfortable hostel. It has a large tall living room with an open fire, and a gallery with elementary double cubicles—and one of the best views on the island, South over the tavern and church towards Hartland Point and beyond. All the rooms are lined with wood.

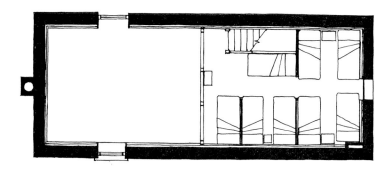

FIRST FLOOR

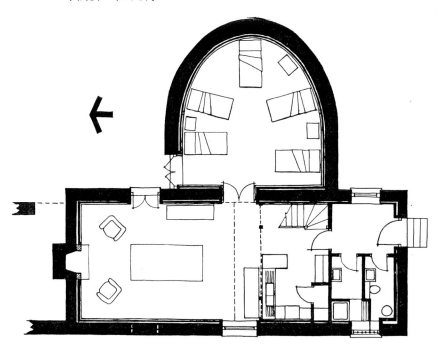

GROUND FLOOR

61

Lundy

The Old Light, designed by Daniel Asher Alexander in 1819, is a most remarkable building. Conceived on a heroic scale and built with Cyclopean blocks of granite, it stands in a truly majestic situation, the highest light in Great Britain. Here the wind rushes with unbroken force from the Atlantic and there is no land to the South West for more than four thousand miles. Inside the keepers' quarters, now a hostel for about a dozen people, the degree of comfort is not of a high order, but in such noble surroundings morale is often terrific.

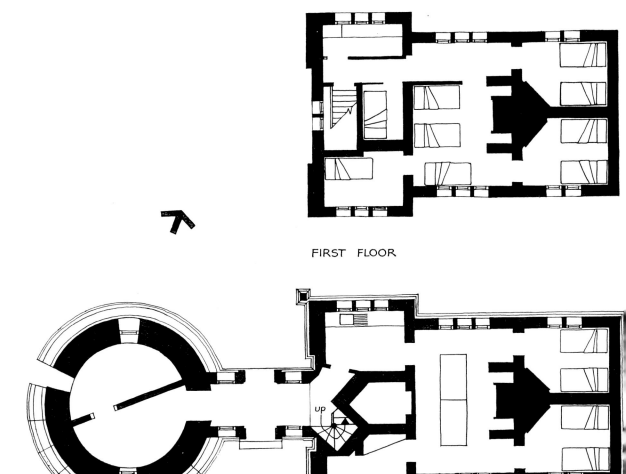

FIRST FLOOR

GROUND FLOOR

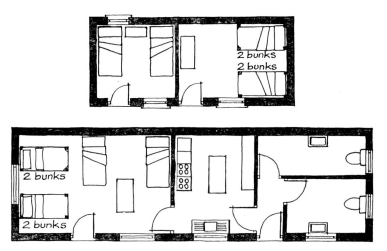

There are also these two detached buildings (known as "East and West") in the compound of the Old Light which will take a party of twelve people.

Landing the mail

Luttrell's Tower

Eaglehurst, Fawley, Southampton

THIS IS AN exceptionally fine eighteenth-century folly, possibly designed by James Wyatt, with whose work at Sheffield Park in 1778 it has affinities. It stands on the shore of the Solent looking towards Cowes; the view, particularly of ships entering and leaving Southampton by the deep water channel, is magnificent—as, in another way, is the sight to landward, from the top floor, of the Fawley refinery and power station.

It was built by Temple Simon Luttrell, a Member of Parliament (but reputedly a smuggler here) who was imprisoned in Paris during the French Revolution and died there in 1803. His sister's marriage to the Duke of Cumberland prompted the Royal Marriages Act of 1772. Luttrell's son-in-law, Lord Cavan, who commanded our forces in Egypt from 1801, became the owner after Luttrell's death, and he brought home with him the two mysterious feet standing on a plinth of black Nubian granite, now at the tower, and thought to be the base of a XIXth dynasty statue of Rameses II.

Thereafter the tower passed through various hands; Queen Victoria nearly bought it (with Eaglehurst House) instead of Osborne, and Marconi used it for his wireless experiments before the 1914 war —a cable he laid still brings electricity to the tower. Sir Clough Williams-Ellis designed the monumental gates and double staircase which give access to it from the beach, too grand really for anyone but Neptune.

We bought the tower in 1968 when the small estate of which it formed a part was sold. It was already habitable, and until recently we had done little except remove the telephone. Over the years, however, a number of alterations had been made, both inside and out, and these we have now begun to rectify. All the rooms have fine chimney pieces and the top room has fine plaster and shell-work as well. There is a tunnel from the basement to the beach, perhaps made for the smuggling

Member. We also have a large boathouse (built for Marconi) which visitors can use.

Luttrells Tower has all the magic of a place where trees—especially yews and ilexes as here—come right down to the sea, and it is easily our most popular place, occupied without fail all the year round.

From the logbook

"Anyone who has the slightest interest in marine activity must come to Luttrell's Tower".

"Just sitting inside and enjoying the rooms themselves was our main pleasure".

"We lit a fire on the beach, cooked sausages, and sat until it was dark".

"At Fawley parish church . . . they tried to rope me into the choir".

"If the QE2 comes in at night she is worth waking the children up to see".

"The light has a wonderful quality here".

"I caught bass on the beach; they take rag, lug and squid".

"We did something different every day, but whatever it was we did was rounded off with the special pleasure of returning to the tower".

"We whispered up and down the tower".

"Fawley residents can be seen taking their dogs for a breath of fresh mono-polydihydroethylene on Sundays . . . perhaps in years to come Landmark will preserve that 20th century folly and open it to anyone that's left".

"How pleasant to stay in three large rooms which have 360° panoramas at three different levels".

"Explore the second floor ceiling by lying in bed with binoculars: well worth a little trouble".

Luttrell's Tower

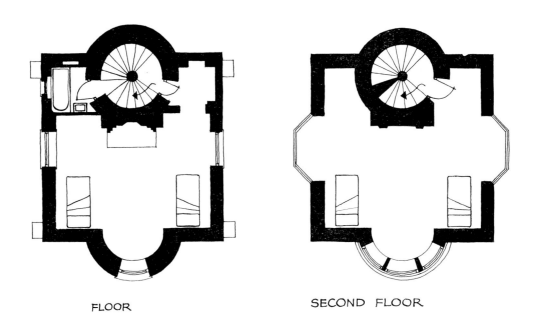

FLOOR

SECOND FLOOR

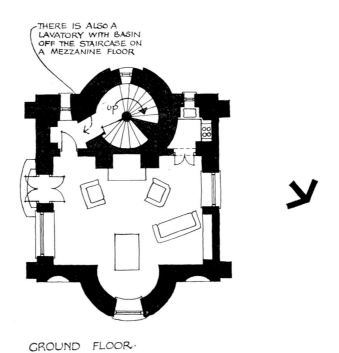

THERE IS ALSO A LAVATORY WITH BASIN OFF THE STAIRCASE ON A MEZZANINE FLOOR

GROUND FLOOR.

Luttrell's Tower

"Why leave the vicinity of the tower? A floating dock sinks before our very eyes. A yacht is driven on to the beach with us being instrumental in calling out the coastguard".

"We wonder who was the owner of the little dog Max whose grave is under the big trees near the washing line".

"The tower has been a joy to live in and to return to each evening."

"Repeated cries from above of 'Quick, Mummy—it's a big ship!' are marvellous for legs and waistline".

"What more suitable place to discover again the pleasures of radio".

"Catherine, Rhodri, me and daddy all streaked into the sea as the coast is so private".

"Fine old hangars at Calshot Castle if you avoid the police there".

"The nicest way to spend the day is to stay here".

"Our children signalled with torches at smugglers off shore who obligingly kept up a ceaseless signalling in return".

"The feeling of living in real rooms".

"We hired out the deck chairs to passers by".

"If there are no fish fingers guillemots will eat raw mince".

"The collection of books of local interest adds to the enjoyment—all sorts of fascinating details, with wider overtones, emerge in this way".

"A very pleasant week for four old codgers".

"QE2 was observed by night, by day, and from Hythe Ferry (it only remains actually to travel in her)".

"There are not many places that are equally enjoyable second time round".

Margells
Fountain Head, Branscombe, Devon

FROM OUTSIDE this is just a plain stone house with a roof of thatch, pleasant enough if unremarkable; but inside it is another matter. The broad passage running across the middle of the house has late medieval oak partitions on each side, and both the downstairs rooms have heavily moulded oak ceilings, probably of the early sixteenth century. Upstairs the rooms are all open to the roof, and in one of them is a contemporary wall painting.

The staircase has solid oak treads and all the doorways are of well above average quality for the time. It is a very strong, interesting and well preserved interior, quite one of the best we have.

What is all this doing in so small a house? It may have been fitted up for some offshoot of an important family— that is one suggestion; but, if so, then one of the downstairs rooms must have been used for cooking, which seems most

Margells

unlikely with such splendid ceilings. Probably Margells is the cross-wing of a medieval house the rest of which has disappeared, as at Hole Cottage. Whatever the explanation, the result is exceptionally satisfying, as all those who stay here will discover.

Moreover the surroundings are extremely pleasant. Margells is one of a group of old cottages, which includes a distinctly agreeable pub. Near the house a little stream of water comes out of a spout in the wall and flows away under the road. Opposite, over the roofs, a wood climbs up a hill, and beyond that is the sea.

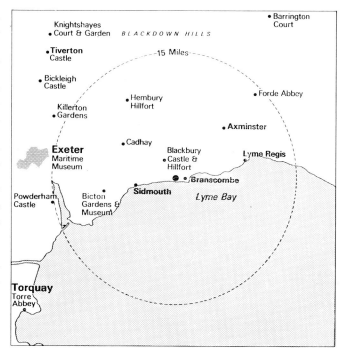

Before

Margells

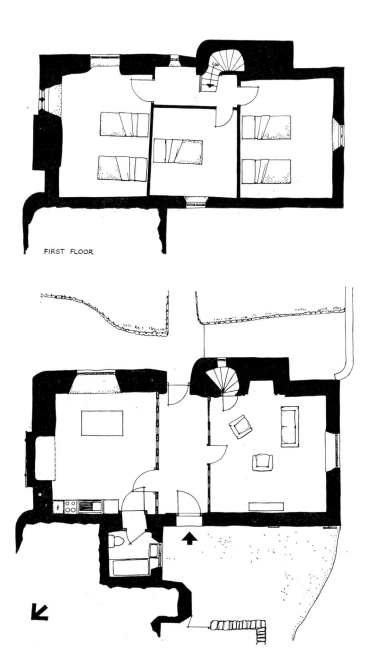

FIRST FLOOR

Appleton Water Tower
Nr. King's Lynn, Norfolk

WE HAVE BEEN GIVEN a long lease of this exceptional Victorian building by a public-spirited local landowner. There is seldom an opportunity to preserve a functional building such as this, let alone one of such quality. As originally constructed, there was on the ground and first floor a dwelling for the person in charge of the tower, and a viewing room reached by a separate outside stair on the second. The flues from all the fireplaces were led through the centre of the iron tank to prevent the water from freezing — a typically Victorian idea, original, simple and practical.

The tower rises from a stretch of grass surrounded by a shelter belt, mainly of yew, and looks very splendid indeed. There is a fine spiral stair of cast iron leading from the viewing room to the top of the tank, which is gravelled, with an elaborate cast iron railing. From here (and from the room below) there is a view on all sides over miles of this wide, open landscape, with a distant gleam of the Wash.

Appleton Water Tower

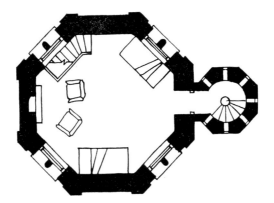

SECOND FLOOR.

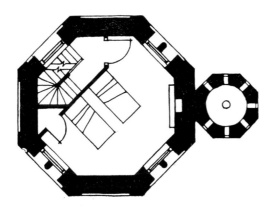

FIRST FLOOR

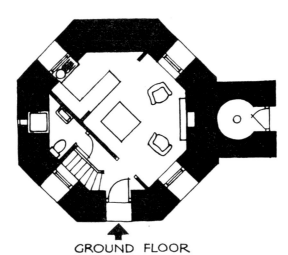

GROUND FLOOR

Marshal Wade's House
14 Abbey Churchyard, Bath

THIS IS NO VERNACULAR AFFAIR, as so many of our places are, but a sophisticated building of about 1720 (early for Bath) in the very centre of the town. Lord Burling-ton designed Wade's London house, and it has been suggested that he designed this house for him also. Whether he did or not, and it seems unlikely, it is a building of

Marshal Wade's House

very high quality. We have restored the windows to their correct design, put back the glazing bars in the shop front, and decluttered and restored all the interiors. As at Penzance, the National Trust has taken the shop—an excellent use for it.

The second floor rooms have good panelling, fireplaces and grates, and all the windows look along the West front of the Abbey, with not a vehicle in sight. From here, on a level with the angels, you can see the great carving of Jacob's ladder. There is also an exceptional view from the bathroom, and from the bath.

All around there are more good things to see within walking distance than anywhere else in Britain. Leave your car behind; come by train, live over the shop, and just be in Bath.

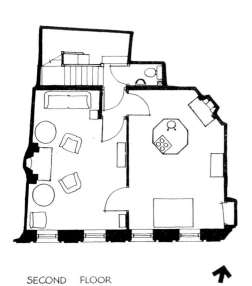

SECOND FLOOR

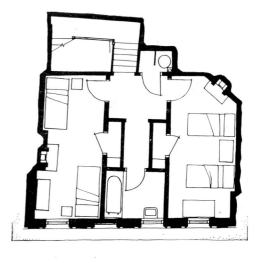

THIRD FLOOR

The Martello Tower
Aldeburgh, Suffolk

THIS IS THE LARGEST and most northerly of the chain of towers put up by the Board of Ordnance to keep out Napoleon. Built in the shape of a quatrefoil for four heavy guns, nearly a million bricks were used in its construction. It stands at the root of the Orford Ness peninsula, between the River Alde and the sea, a few hundred yards from Aldeburgh. We bought it, sadly damaged, in 1971, with eight acres of saltings.

We have removed the derelict twentieth-century superstructure, repaired the outer brickwork and parapet (a tremendous job) and restored the vaulted interior, which has a floor of teak. Here you may live with the sea, the wind sometimes, the light at Orford Ness flashing at night, and Aldeburgh at just the right distance. Amber and bloodstones, brought by glaciers from Scandinavia, have been found on the beach. In January people fish by night with Tilley lamps and canvas shelters. Many visitors bring sailing dinghies.

From the logbook

"From the moment we came through the door in the gathering dusk we knew it was going to be a marvellous experience".

"On Friday we were at last able to hoist our standard—made of an old blue sheet —from the flagstaff, where it looked terrific".

"Theberton church has a piece of Zeppelin in the porch".

"Real solid furniture to go with the real solid tower".

"I am afraid our beagle ate several pieces of the jigsaw".

78

The Martello Tower

"The Ouija board revealed the presence of a spirit".

"The door bell rang at 5 o'clock on Sunday–the Rt. Hon. Jeremy Thorpe and family".

"Today we swam only once".

"November: fish stew on the roof for Sunday lunch".

"Fifteen of us sat round the table with not too much shoving".

"We watched an eclipse of the moon from the roof".

"We added to the atmosphere by bringing some of our antique weapons, and our bear".

"Games and talk happily replaced the goggle box".

"Most lasting memory: the sea".

Before restoration

The Martello Tower

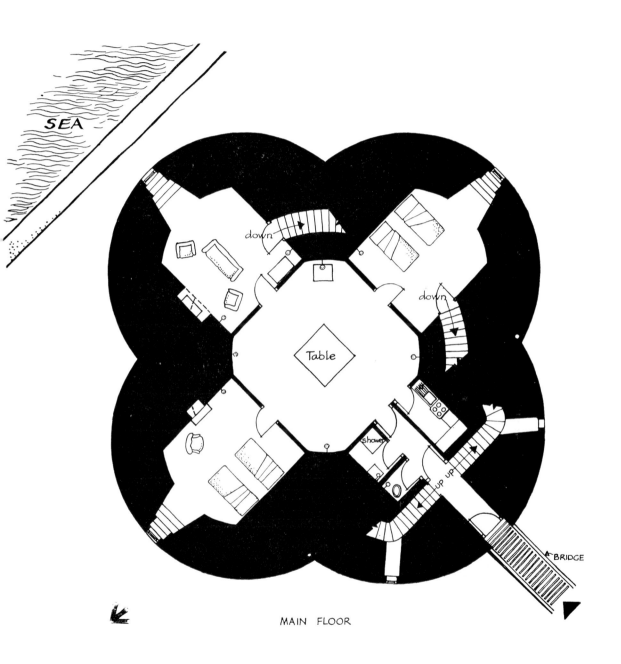

SEA

Table

down

down

Shower

UP UP

BRIDGE

MAIN FLOOR

The Music Room
Sun Street, Lancaster

THIS IS ONE of the most difficult and worthwhile places we have tackled. The Music Room had been well known for years as a building in distress, but nothing could be done because it had other buildings up against it on all four sides. On our first visit we had to reach it by walking through the toy warehouse of which it formed a part, and we had to buy (a long job) four other buildings and demolish them to give the builders access.

It seems to have been built about 1730, as a garden house, but its surroundings have long since been overlaid with streets. In the nineteenth century the Music Room was part of a lighting and heating works, and there are harrowing accounts of "the terrible ravages of machine and smith work" and of the "damage caused by the rearing of timber and pipes" against the plasterwork. Later it was a stained glass studio. When we arrived it had a temporary roof of asbestos sheeting, and many broken windows. Most of the plasterwork had fallen, but luckily almost all of it was still in the building.

We have turned the loggia on the ground

Before

The Music Room

floor into a shop, by removing a floor which had been inserted into it. It did not seem practical to leave this large space open and empty in the middle of a town, and we hope that a shop will bring life to the Music Room's surroundings. In order not to spoil the Ionic triumphal arch in the centre, we have glazed it with a single enormous pane.

The plasterwork of the music room itself has taken 6000 hours of work to repair. It is an exceptional baroque interior. On the walls are the muses of eloquence, history, music, astronomy, tragedy, rhetoric, dancing, comedy and amorous poetry, with their attributes; over the fireplace Apollo; in the cove trophies of arms and emperors; and on the upper cornices, birds and baskets of flowers. A fruitful goddess with a torch presides over the ceiling—but it is really the muses' room, of which its present name is doubtless a corruption.

One muse, Terpsichore, had vanished entirely and she has been re-created by the plasterers from Sutton Coldfield as a modern girl, big and busty, with a cheerful eye, and an excellent muse of dancing she makes.

In the attic above, reached by a narrow stair, we have made a flat. From it and from the roof there are distant views over Lancaster (including a fine view of the Castle from the sink); and at all times, waiting for you to enter it, there is the stillness of the music room below, both full and empty at the same time, as is the way with rich interiors.

Outside, having demolished the buildings attached to the front of the Music Room, we have sold the space thus created to the City (for less than a third of what it has cost us, somewhat to our irritation) and it is being turned into a pedestrian square.

Lancaster is a really fine town, with many things worth attention—not least Rennie's monumental aqueduct on the Lancaster canal, bridging the River Lune like a vestige of imperial Rome.

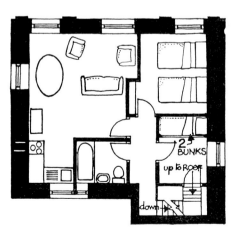

The New Inn
Peasenhall, Saxmundham, Suffolk

THE LOCAL AUTHORITY bought this row of ten cottages and a shop, then very dilapidated, with a view to demolishing them; but, on realizing their importance, had a praiseworthy change of heart and sold them to us—and indeed later gave us a welcome grant. The centre of the range is a late medieval hall-house, in use as an inn by 1478. Although derelict, almost the whole medieval building had survived, in particular the carved door-heads at the service end of the hall, and the crown posts of hall and solar.

We have repaired the hall (which is now open to the public) and all the other cottages as well. The three oldest of these, which are not very suitable for permanent occupation, we have kept as Landmarks. Two of them, at each end of the medieval hall, are entered by crossing the floor of

the hall, as they would have been originally. The high end is the grander, with one particularly fine bedroom—the medieval solar. At the backs of the cottages we have removed a number of decayed out-buildings and made an elementary garden and a space where cars can be hidden.

Peasenhall is a long, open village, scene of a famous murder in 1902, when murder was rare enough to be thought very shocking. It is well supplied with shops, one of which, and a very nice one, is in the row which we own. The Real Ale people are very complimentary about the beer (Adnam's). Heveningham Hall, by James Wyatt, one of the most magnificent of all country houses, is within walking distance, about half of the way being through the park. Here some of our visitors (they write) were locked in, and had to get out by rolling under the gates, yet another life-enhancing Landmark Trust experience.

From the logbook

"A delight to wake up to and return to each day".

"The best part of our weekend here was the banquet on Sunday evening. We collected greenery from the hedgerows and decorated the Hall with it. The tables from both houses were made into one long one and both mothers prepared a super feast. In one corner sat the minstrels who were—me (oboe), Deborah (flute) and Nikki (cello). After the first course in the candlelit Hall the minstrels played some chamber music, and God Save the Queen; we then feasted on two Christmas puddings, Tom got the penny. After the meal was some frantic cleaning up (though nothing was smashed) and soon the Hall looked as if nothing had happened —it was rather sad really".

"The bacon at Emmett's Stores is By Appointment to H.M. The Queen Mother".

"We found the taps a bit stiff, otherwise

the restoration was very well done".

"If you are not very fond of your children take them on the wall-walk at Framlingham Castle".

"A seal swam by me at Thorpeness— I thought it was an old man".

"We will have to come back to continue reading the books".

Before

87

The New Inn

SECOND FLOOR

HIGH END

upper part of
HALL

down

LOW END

FIRST FLOOR

N

HIGH END

HALL

c. c.

up

down

NEW INN
COTTAGE

up

LOW END

GROUND FLOOR

Crown post of the solar

10 North Street
Cromford, Derbyshire

NORTH STREET, A CUL-DE-SAC off Cromford Hill named after the Prime Minister, was built in 1771 by Richard Arkwright (then aged 39) to house his mill workers. It is the earliest planned industrial housing in the world, and the finest of its type ever built—vastly superior to the industrial housing of the nineteenth century. The three-storey gritstone houses have one room on each floor, with a room for framework-knitting in the attic. Each house has a small garden, and an allotment at a distance. At the end of the street is the school, built by the same family in 1832.

The Arkwrights sold the property in 1924 and in 1961 it was bought by the Matlock Urban District Council with a view to demolition. The Derbyshire County Council, to their great credit, would not permit this, and consequently the Matlock UDC sold six houses to the Ancient Monuments Society—which in 1974 offered them to us. We have also bought a further three houses in the street, and two other buildings which seem to have been originally a public house and shop, though latterly used together as an institute or meeting room. We thus now own most of one side of the street.

We have re-roofed and improved the nine houses, reorganising their kitchens and washhouses at the back, putting in bathrooms, and restoring the long windows of the attic workrooms. We have kept the original interiors where they have survived.

One house, which was empty when we bought it, we have repaired as a Landmark so that people can live in and appreciate this much inhabited street, and explore its remarkable surroundings. Here you will be what the traveller should be, in a tiny minority, an object of interest, not part of an unwanted herd.

For those at all interested in industrial history, there is a great deal to see—lead

10 North Street

mines, the Cromford canal, the High Peak Railway, Arkwright's mills, and traces of the life they all created. There is also Matlock Bath, and Matlock, a spectacular and very genuine old inland resort, at whose petrifying wells you can have your bowler hat turned into stone.

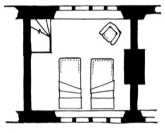

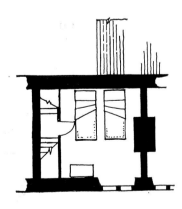

SECOND FLOOR

FIRST FLOOR

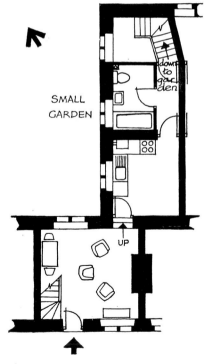

SMALL GARDEN

GROUND FLOOR

The Old Grammar School
Kirby Hill, Nr. Richmond, Yorkshire

BUILT IN THE DISCOURAGING REIGN of Queen Mary—a rare time to be founding a school—this is one of a group of stone buildings with stone roofs which surround the village green of Kirby Hill, in a severe but beautiful landscape. The Trust which owns both the school and the almshouses opposite was instituted by Dr. Dakyn on the eleventh of May 1556. After the Mass of the Holy Ghost he preached in English from the text "Nisi Dominus aedificaverit domum" and then explained to a numerous congregation how the Wardens of the Trust were to be chosen. On the feast of the Decollation of St. John the names of six respectable parishioners were to be written on slips of paper, and enclosed in balls of clay. These were to be put into a jar of water. Two names were then to be drawn, and the jar of water with the remaining names put away in a cupboard which he also provided. If a vacancy occurred during the year, a further ball of clay was to be drawn from the jar and opened. All this is still done, and the jar is still kept in his cupboard, which is a very handsome one.

In 1957, after a life of 401 years, his school was overtaken by progress and closed. The Trustees have given us a long lease of it; we have repaired the ground floor schoolroom in the hope that it will be used as a village hall, and the sixteenth century lodging of the master, upstairs, we have turned into a flat. It has one particularly fine bedroom, looking into the churchyard. There is also a large library of old school books (in the building when we arrived) and a general atmosphere of ancient peace, abetted by the church clock which has a tranquillising strike.

The Old Grammar School

From the logbook

"Walk down Deepdale through Applegarth to the river. Down and back is a pleasant three hours if you have small children, particularly if you spend an hour splashing about in the springs at the bottom".

"There are some carvings of mice on the base of the altar rails, and on some footstools by the altar".

"The dale covered in snow viewed from the living room window is a sight to behold"

"The friendly residents of Kirby Hill are more than willing to talk to visitors about the interesting tales, past and present, of village life".

"Watching the lambs being born has been most exciting".

"Returning each evening to a comfortable warm flat with such a good atmosphere was a real pleasure. Thank you to all who plan and work to give us so much to remember and look forward to".

"An interesting approach to the Haworth parsonage is by the Keighley and Worth Valley steam railway".

"Mrs Chapman (the milk) told us of a funeral here some years ago when the hearse got snowed-up and the coffin had to continue by sledge".

"We did have rather a lovely walk today beside the river in Richmond, gradually climbing upwards through crackling leaves".

"We found six carved mice in the church; they are the trade mark of Robert Thompson's craftsmen of Kilburn near Helmsley".

"It is possible to walk to Richmond without climbing a wall or any fence without a stile".

"We had a most interesting visit from the vicar who told us some of the history of this building".

"Hardraw Force: do go behind the fall —it is not as dangerous as it looks (entrance through pub but only 4p)".

"We came without transport—train and two bus rides from London".

"The caretaker and her friends in Washton made us very welcome and we were invited into a considerable series of parties".

"The selection of old school books exceeded all expectations. They brought back memories long since forgotten, and provided information never known".

The Old Grammar School

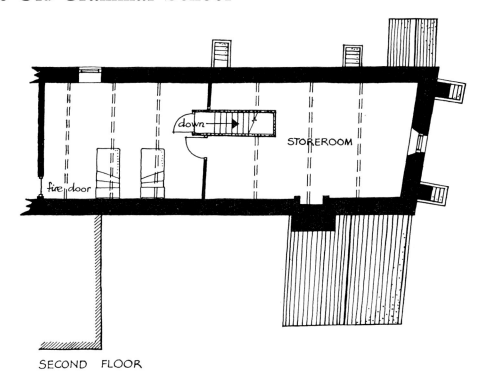

SECOND FLOOR

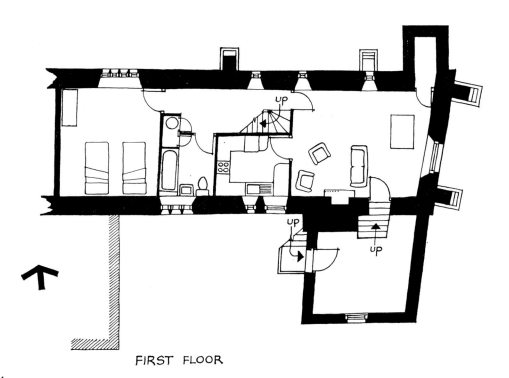

FIRST FLOOR

The Gothic Temple
Stowe, Buckingham

THIS TEMPLE, built about 1740 of Northamptonshire ironstone, is part of the eighteenth-century landscape planned by William Kent at Stowe, where by good fortune he had the young Lancelot ("Capability") Brown as gardener. It was designed by James Gibbs; his original drawings for it are in the Ashmolean Museum at Oxford. Inside, the rooms have moulded stone pilasters and plaster vaults —the main vault of the central space being painted with elaborate heraldic achievements. To be on the first floor gallery is an important architectural experience; and at the top of the staircase there is a belvedere with stone seats and a fine view over this former demesne of the Dukes of Buckingham.

The building had been used as an armoury by the school, and before that by the local militia, but Stowe School, with great kindness, gave us a long lease of it in 1970. We have removed an addition, unblocked the windows and restored the interior. It does have all modern conveniences, if in rather surprising places, and the heating inevitably is not too good; but we hope that the splendour of the temple and its surroundings will compensate those who stay here.

For some reason people seem particularly to enjoy the Gothic Temple, and this must be due in part to the school who —when there is no reason whyever they should—often allow our visitors to swim, play tennis, use the school shops (which are very good) and attend "occasional concerts at the Queen's Temple". They

The Gothic Temple

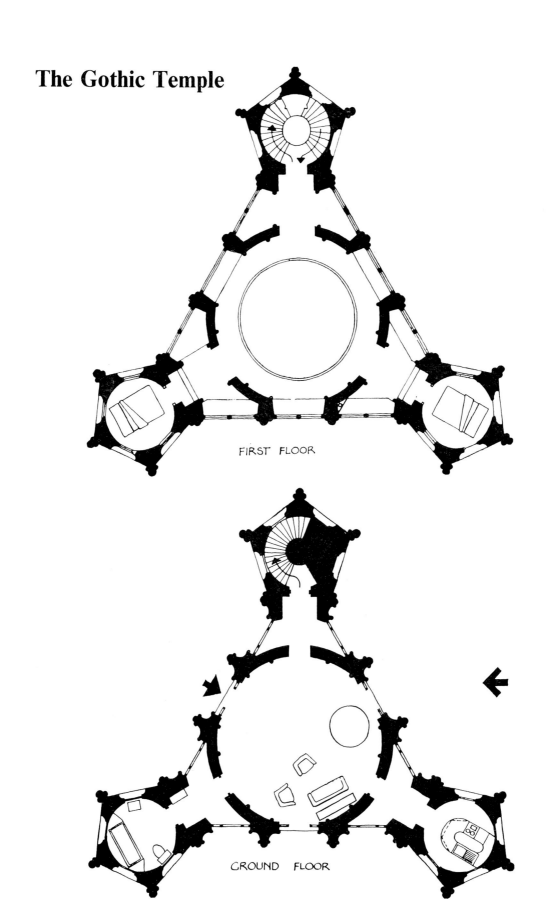

FIRST FLOOR

GROUND FLOOR

The Gothic Temple

have also allowed, or condoned, use of their assault course. One visitor put his wife round, but she failed to make it, falling at the stream. For all this we are indeed grateful.

From the logbook

"Looking out of the windows in complete contentment".

"... three hundred schoolboys, dressed in army uniforms firing rifles and letting off maroons".

"We were welcomed wherever we went".

"Our dog enjoyed the boys' assault course".

"Had a bonza visit catching up on our colonial heritage".

"We were somewhat dismayed to see figures flitting from tree to tree with machine guns".

"An enjoyable weekend rescuing a hedgehog from the bottom of the cattle-grid".

"Half a dozen people arrived by van, produced a balloon, and flew off in it ... a lovely view from the tower as they drifted away".

"Warm days and moonlit nights ... the comfort of owls and bells".

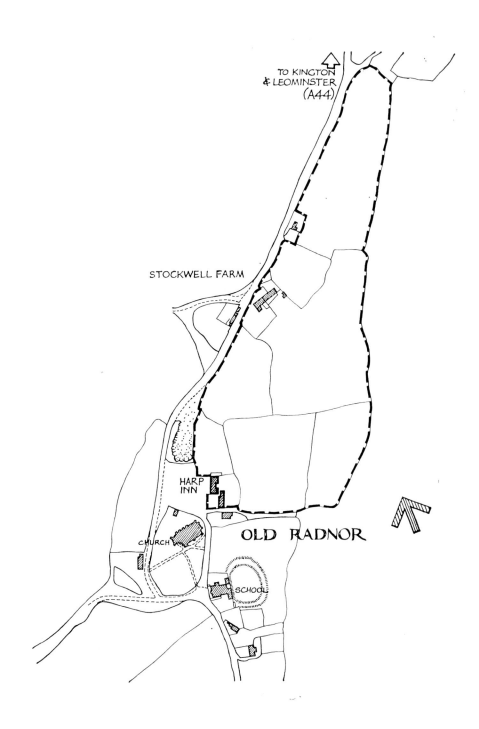

TO KINGTON
& LEOMINSTER
(A44)

STOCKWELL FARM

HARP
INN

CHURCH

OLD RADNOR

SCHOOL

Old Radnor

Presteigne, Powys
The Harp Inn

OLD RADNOR consists of a few scattered cottages, a surprisingly large fifteenth-century church containing the oldest organ case in Britain, and the Harp Inn—all grouped on a hillside overlooking Radnor Forest and the valley of the Lugg. Charles II is known to have been here, since he complained about the food.

We have removed various additions to the building, and have replaced the corrugated iron and slate roof with the original stone. Besides the dining room and slate-flagged bar there are four bedrooms, three bathrooms and a sitting room.

Between the Harp and Stockwell Farm below we own about fifteen acres of land which visitors are welcome to use. It is a quite particularly attractive hillside of rough fields, full of mysterious hollows and green hummocks, anthills, thorn bushes and other unfunctional things.

From the logbook

"If you climb high up the hill behind the Inn you can, when there is blasting in the local quarries, hear a strange and urgent sound in the air, as if flights of arrows were passing overhead".

"We shall miss everyone in the snug, the darts, the log fire and the company, the beautiful walks and the welcome peace".

Old Radnor
Stockwell Farm

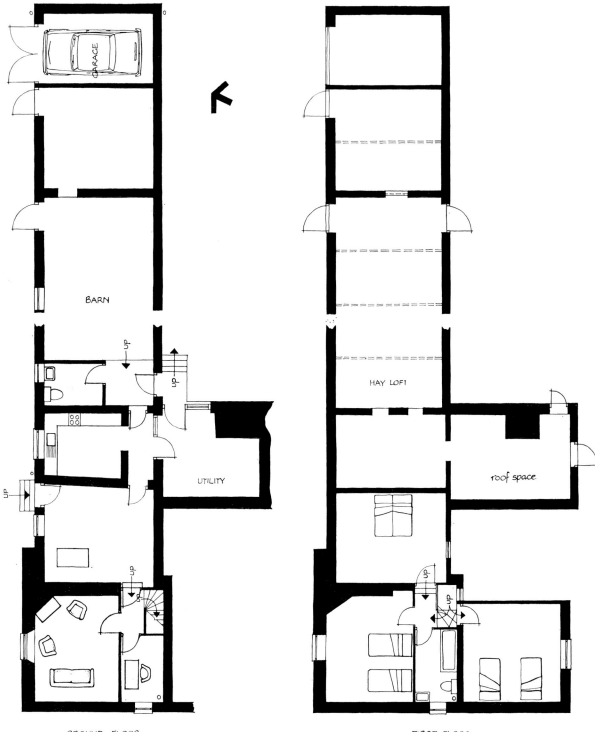

GROUND FLOOR

FIRST FLOOR

Old Radnor

Stockwell Farm

THIS STONE AND timber-framed farmhouse does not look much from outside, but it has a medieval core, the central truss of the hall showing in one of the bedrooms. It also has a beautiful view; and behind are our hill fields, into which you can turn your children, and across which you can walk up to the Harp.

One of our visitors at Stockwell Farm had been here before, as a child evacuated from wartime London ("dumped late at night with strangers") and has left a moving account in the logbook: "Missing are the neighbours who came to stare at the new children ... Missing too the central fire, the cake hissing on the girdle ... the hideous steamy Mondays ... and the grisly boiled pig and tapioca", etc. Some February visitors got some skiing.

From the logbook

"We tried to walk up Harley Dingle as recommended, but it is rather disconcert-ing to see blazing shells crossing the valley and thumping into the hillside".

"It seems strange to think we have only been here a week".

"We were very grateful for the carefully chosen library. Such attention to detail, including the map with local footpaths, makes us loyal and admiring adherents of the Landmark Trust".

"At 90p an hour I rode a small willing furry pony all over the hills".

"Strongly recommended: Songs of Praise at Old Radnor church and Guy Fawkes Night procession at Presteigne".

"We have enjoyed the farm and the insight it gives one into the lives of our ancestors".

"The mechanism of the clock in the bell tower at Pembridge is most interesting and well worth a visit".

"We were driven by curiosity to see the disused military hospital at Kington and

Old Radnor

found the overgrown wards now occupied by calves and turkeys".

"We would love to return here: the lack of clutter is a pleasure to experience".

"For botanists; there is a very good bog at Tregaron".

"Kington is certainly to be recommended for its shopping if only to savour the pleasantries passed, people talking to each other by name, friendly welcomes—how different from our supermarket".

"Many pleasant surprises for the traveller by foot".

"We have found Stockwell Farm charming . . . . We would love to come again but it is a long way from Adelaide".

"The vicar called on horseback".

"We spent a fascinating morning searching out the remains of the Leominster canal".

"It was an interesting experience to

walk the ancient paths across the wildness of the ridges, where I particularly enjoyed the lark song".

"It is with very sad hearts that we leave not only this lovely place, but also the people in it".

Sanders
Lettaford, North Bovey, Devon

LETTAFORD CONSISTS OF three farmhouses (of which Sanders is one) and a Methodist chapel, round a small green on the edge of Dartmoor. The public road which leads to it here breaks up into tracks. Sanders is a late-medieval Devon long-house arranged on the usual plan of inner room, hall, cross-passage and shippon, all under one roof with a shouldered granite porch originally used as entrance by both cattle and people. The walls are made of blocks of granite ashlar, some of them enormous.

It must have started life as a house of high quality, more important than a farmhouse, but it declined into a labourer's cottage long enough ago to avoid damaging improvements. The kitchen range (a Bungalow Belle of 1931) is the most recent piece of modernisation.

The farm buildings and the small ancient enclosures of Sanders are also interesting—as is the whole of this very early settlement on the fringes of the moor.

Sanders

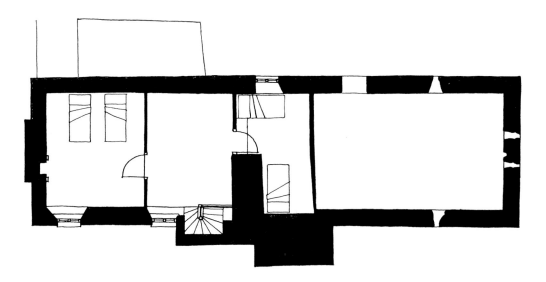

FIRST FLOOR

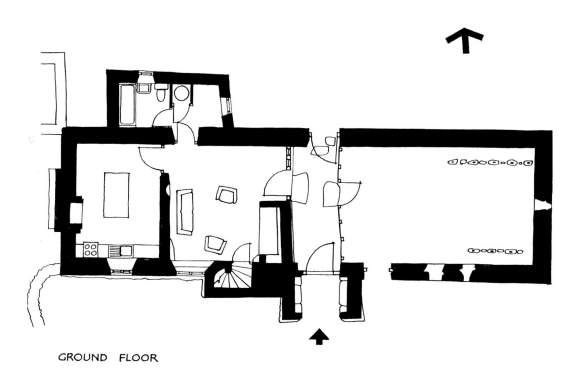

GROUND FLOOR

Sanders

Plas Uchaf

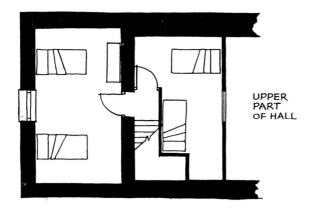

FIRST FLOOR

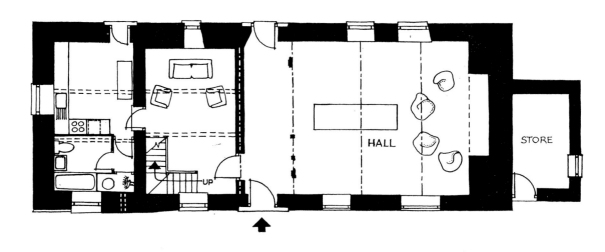

GROUND FLOOR

Plas Uchaf
Llangar, nr. Corwen, Clwyd

THIS IS THE ancestral home of the family of Hughes of Gwerclas, descendants of Iorwerth, third son of Owain Brogyntyn. It is a substantial medieval hall-house built about 1400, or perhaps before, on the side of a low hill in the Dee valley. Very few houses of this age and type survive in Wales, and the quality of the work at Plas Uchaf is exceptionally good.

It was in the last stages of dereliction when we arrived on the scene, but the oak frames of medieval houses are remarkably tough, particularly where they have been smoked for generations by the open hearth. Although it had been exposed to the rain for several years, repair was possible, and well worth while.

The hall is surprisingly grand, with a spere truss, two other moulded trusses, traces of a louvre, and wind and ridge braces—a roof of quite sophisticated carpentry. In the sixteenth century an immense fireplace was added. The fire and

the hall are the twin spirits of Plas Uchaf, and at night, with the wooden ribs of the hall moving a little in the firelight, you can imagine that you are Jonah inside the whale.

From the logbook

"It would be an experience to live in a hall house. We have now achieved that ambition and have not been disappointed".

"The huge log fires at night are lovely after a day walking".

"We have had to go out to buy wood, and so met people".

"The farm at Ty Fos has a prehistoric stone circle in the front garden".

"You can't really appreciate the hall without the smell and light of the fire".

"We had some splendid walks on the hills behind Cynwyd, covered with a light

108

Plas Uchaf

sprinkling of snow, with terrific views of Snowdon and Moel Siabhod glittering in the sun".

"The new oak cupboard which marks the first ten years of the Trust is a fine piece of modern craftsmanship".

"Glorious clear Autumn days with enormous log fires in the hall every evening".

"We've spent the week finding out just where we are in the neighbourhood".

"We walked up to Caer Drewyn: here Owen Gwynedd prepared to repel the invasion of Henry II".

".... It is a large, prosperous-looking farm. They greet you as you enter: 'Is it logs?' and you say 'It is logs, if you please'. 30p for a heavy bag of huge oak logs, which burn slowly and strongly, like coal. On Friday night we dined in the hall and had a huge fire and watched the patterns the flames made on the timbers: it lasted more than ten hours".

"Everyone should spend Christmas here —well, at least we should again, and perhaps will".

"We had a great blaze in the hall to celebrate our last evening".

The Pineapple
Dunmore, Airth, Stirlingshire

THE PINEAPPLE IS an elaborate summer house of two storeys, built in 1761 for the 29-year-old Earl of Dunmore (later Governor of New York and Virginia). Though classical and orthodox at ground level, it grows slowly into something entirely vegetable; conventional architraves put out shoots and end up as prickly leaves of stone. It is an eccentric work, but of undoubted genius, and built of the very finest masonry Every leaf is drained to prevent damage by frost.

It presides over an immense walled garden, made by the Dunmores at a good Scottish distance from their house—now ruined, but just visible, with the hills behind, from the Pineapple's north front. All the walls of this garden are honeycombed with flues, and there were furnaces every few yards behind them, those nearest to the Pineapple having their chimneys disguised as urns. To house some of those who tended all this, a stone bothy looking over the garden was built on each side of the Pineapple. These we have re-roofed and made very comfortable.

The Pineapple and its surroundings (now open to the public) were given by Lord and Lady Perth to the National Trust for Scotland; we have taken a long lease of the whole and have restored garden, garden walls, and pineapple, with the help of handsome grants from the Historic Buildings Council and the Tourist Board—who made it a condition of their grant that we should build a public lavatory in this remote, well-wooded spot. This, after obtaining planning permission

and byelaw approval from the Falkirk District Council, and having received the observations of the Principal Environmental Health Officer for the Eastern Division, together with a waiver, after negotiation, of the requirement to provide, *inter alia*, hot water, artificial lighting, and an incinerator, we have done, at a cost of £4460, thus keeping alive the spirit here of lavish eccentricity.

From the logbook

"There is a hermit's cave nearby. It is hidden in a clump of rhododendron bushes and contains a chimney and a bed ... We met a local gentleman exercising his greyhound who kindly showed us the route".

"Another pursuit was spotting the old stones of former houses (including the ship from the Ship Inn) incorporated into more recently built houses in Airth".

"The experience of actually living in such a building is so much more rewarding than merely visiting".

"We were very reluctant to leave the Pineapple".

"Dunmore Pottery has only an old kiln visible and has not operated for at least 50 years. Once famous for teapots".

"Farewell, old fruit".

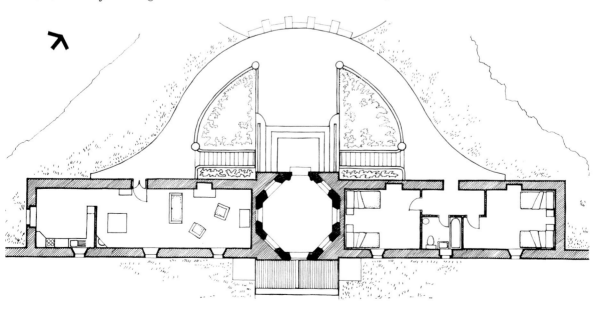

Purton Green
Stansfield, Sudbury, Suffolk

PURTON GREEN IS ONE of the many lost villages of Suffolk, where generations spent their lives, but now just patches of lime and fragments in the plough. It lies on an old road south from Bury St. Edmunds, today hardly a path. All that remains is this timber-framed hall-house, built about 1250 and therefore an extreme rarity. The hall is aisled on both sides, with scissor-braced trusses, and there are probably no more than half a dozen comparable houses in the country; clearly it was once an important place, from the details and mouldings which survive in it.

When we were able to buy it in 1969 it had been empty for many years and was little more than a ruin partly covered with decaying thatch. As with almost all medieval houses, a floor and chimney stack had later been inserted in the hall, but these additions were so derelict that

we felt justified in removing them. As a result this rare hall can be experienced very much in its original state—even with some of the medieval thatching spars still blackened by smoke from the open hearth. Part of the house—the high end of the hall—was rebuilt about 1600 to a standard well above the average and this we have turned into living quarters.

Because of its condition we have had to do more work to the building than we liked, but we have made no attempt to make the new look old. We have neither treated it as a museum specimen, to be left uninhabitable, nor faked it up as a film set. New wood and metal have been used, and left with their machine finish. Time will work on them, but the visitor will be able to see what is old and what is new.

The living quarters can only be reached

through the hall, and those who stay at Purton Green must therefore cross and recross the hall, as their predecessors have done for seven hundred years. Indeed it is clear from the logbook that the hall plays, as it always has, an important part in the lives of those who stay here—they eat in it, and act; they decorate it for Christmas; someone flew a falcon in it; others played shuttlecock in it; one party wrote "we found ourselves performing a circle dance". It is not recorded that anyone has yet had the courage to read *Beowulf* in it.

A car cannot be got closer than four hundred yards, and that involves crossing a ford; but we provide a wheelbarrow for the rest of the journey ("The wheelbarrow is lovely"—Logbook). The house stands now in the middle of fields, surrounded by the life of the fields, with ordinary unchanging Suffolk countryside, marvellously unimproved, in all directions.

From the logbook

"The sheer joy of staggering up the dark and windy path".

"We felt exhilarated by the interior spaces".

"The isolation has been welcomed by us all".

"A warm welcome at the 'Compasses'; they take a great interest in the inhabitants of this house".

"As we were walking we startled a hare who ran into the field where the tips of his ears were showing".

"Lavenham has amazing unspoiled streets with no yellow lines, zebra crossings, traffic signs or street lights".

"Nothing but birds and walks".

"A troupe of players appeared at the door out of the mist and offered entertainment in return for fare. They played their piece in the Hall, Treason in the Tower, which was applauded vigorously (to keep warm)".

"Thanks to the Landmark for introducing us to all this".

"The Suffolk Hunt came past on Saturday morning and we were able to keep up with them till lunchtime".

"We were content to just be here".

"The clientele of the 'Compasses' recommend the dance to be held in Stansfield village hall on February 15th".

"My brother and I saw a big fox in the field near the moat . . . This place is one of the best places I've been to".

"We trudged along the path, laden like camels with all the necessaries of life".

"Cambridge: something here for everyone".

"The hunt came past and sighted their fox in the field behind the barn".

Purton Green

"There are United States air bases at Mildenhall and Lakenheath where they have super aeroplanes".

"Thoroughly enjoyed entertaining the thatchers for coffee this morning".

"Rested and absorbed the atmosphere ... collected some frog spawn".

"The surrounding area is a paradise for beer drinkers".

"The most incredibly decent and civilised bargain".

"It is hard to imagine that people were living in this house long before our own country was even discovered".

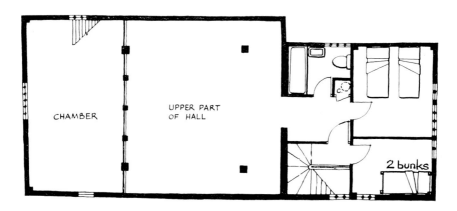

FIRST FLOOR

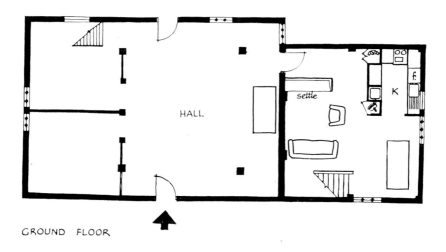

GROUND FLOOR

15 Tower Hill
St. Davids, Dyfed

THIS COTTAGE occupies a most important site. It is built just above the Close wall at St. Davids, and has an astonishing view of the cathedral, facing it squarely at tower level.

The living room has great serenity, with the sun on one side, and the sunlit cathedral on the other. The furniture is very good. Here little need trouble you ("A snail ate a vital part of my message to the milkman"—Logbook) and at your door is the reassurance of cathedral life, its services, the bells, and the building itself. The sea appears to be about a mile away in most directions; the coastal path, with stunning views, encircles St. David's—"a long way, but very good for you".

From the logbook

"We have enjoyed our stay because the car has been out of action for almost two weeks".

"The children enjoyed watching the bellringing in the tower ... spacious belfry and friendly ringers".

"The seals on the beaches with their young are certainly most spectacular".

"The pace of life here in December seems like that of pre-war England—bliss".

"White walls, a faded carpet, and furniture made in a time when things were meant to last".

"I looked at once for this book ... what resourceful and intelligent people frequent the Landmark cottages".

"How helpful to find all the information one usually gleans by the end of a holiday"

"The view from the sink lightens the labours of the housewife".

"We shall be back again, quite soon I think".

15 Tower Hill

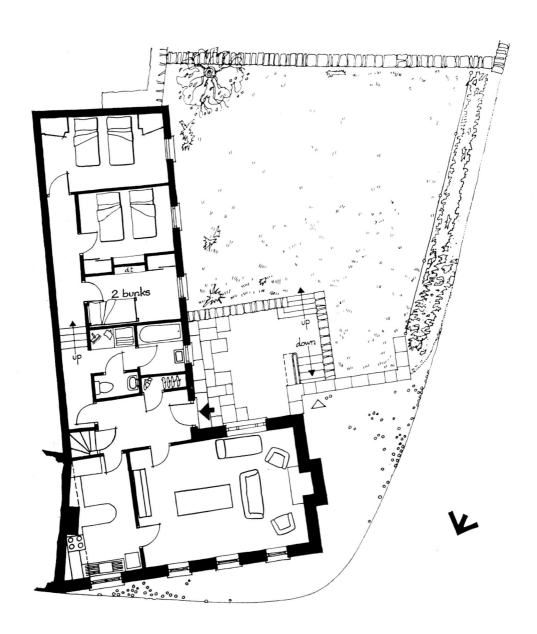

2 bunks

up

down

up

From the kitchen sink

Saddell Castle
Nr. Campbeltown, Argyll

THIS CASTLE, "a fayre pyle, and a stronge", was built by the Bishop of Argyll in 1508. By the end of the century it was firmly in the hands of the Campbells, who held it for nearly four hundred years. It is a fine and complete tower-house with a battlemented wall-walk round the roof; and it stands at the mouth of a little river, facing Arran across Kilbrannan Sound. When we took it there were substantial trees growing from the roof, all the windows had gone, and it had not been inhabited for many years—indeed it has all but fallen into ruin several times in its long life.

Inside, one bedroom has eighteenth century panelling, dilapidated but reparable, and there is a good mid-nineteenth century sitting room. All the windows have deep embrasures and, as usual in such buildings, there are a number of little closets in the thickness of the walls. The floor inside the front door was removable so that unwelcome visitors could fall straight into the prison below.

Many Scottish castles and tower-houses stand alone. Like that they are impressive, but a good deal less interesting than where, as here, the walls of all the outbuildings survive (including part of the barmkin wall itself) round a narrow cobbled yard—dairy, byre, barn, stable, harness room and mill, built hard up against the castle, in the beginning for protection and then left there because the laird never had any money to spare. Indeed all the later structural repairs seem to have been a struggle, done with whatever lay to hand, even old cart axles, used as lintels, and lengths of rail—probably from the Campbeltown and Machrihanish light railway.

Here and there in the castle buildings can also be seen moulded or carved stones from the ruins of Saddell Abbey, a short distance up the valley. Lying on the ground under the trees in this peaceful spot are many graveslabs of the unruly Scots, gripping their long swords or stand-

120

Saddell Castle

ing in their ancient ships of war—a reminder, as is all Saddell, of Scotland's history, half tragic but half splendid as well (like that of Poland) and not English at all.

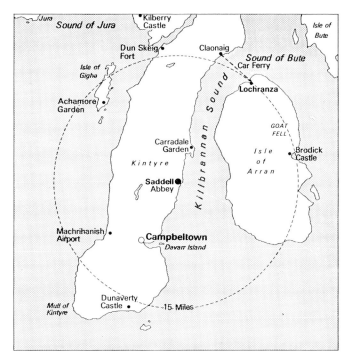

Saddell Castle

SECOND
FLOOR

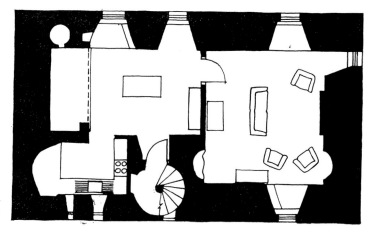

FIRST
FLOOR

GROUND
FLOOR

122

Saddell Castle

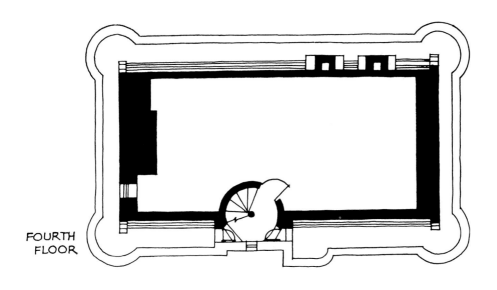

FOURTH
FLOOR

THIRD
FLOOR

Saddell
Shore Cottage

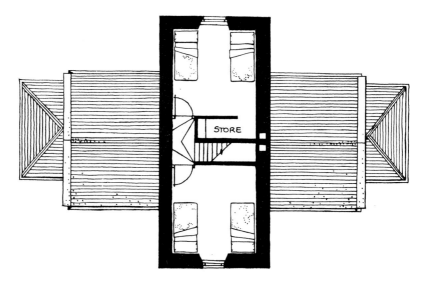

FIRST FLOOR

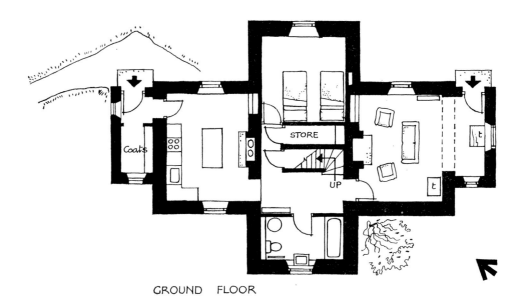

GROUND FLOOR

124

Saddell
Shore Cottage

SHORE COTTAGE LOOKS at the castle across a little bay. It stands on a rocky point, among trees which grow right down to the sea, and is a plain but stylish Victorian building, imaginative in design as well as situation.

From the logbook

"We had no idea when we came that there would be so many people with our surname, Semple, which is not common at home in the United States, but they are all over the place here".

"Overall it compares very favourably with Caernarfon".

"We only made one outing by car, to the vitrified fort at the end of the Carradale peninsula—a marvellous situation with eider duck, and gannets plunging violently into the sea after fish".

"A fire is easily built in the fireplace and brightens up the living room extremely".

"I found a bottle washed up on the shore with a message in it from children in Bute".

"Happy days. We will leave you to discover for yourselves, as therein lies the enjoyment".

30 St. Mary's Lane

Tewkesbury, Gloucestershire

WE HAVE RESTORED two of these eighteenth-century framework knitters' cottages in a lane leading down to the Avon. The stocking makers both lived and worked here, their workshops being on the first floor, with long windows for the light. From them can be seen the marvellous roofscape of Tewkesbury, backing onto

30 St. Mary's Lane

the Avon, and there is a fine urban view of the Abbey along the narrow court behind.

It was Gilbert Scott's drastic proposals for the restoration of Tewkesbury Abbey in 1877 which brought into being the Society for the Protection of Ancient Buildings. Indeed the Abbey, bought by the parishioners at the Dissolution and so saved from the fate of almost all monastic churches, is a formidable monument to independence of spirit, as all who enter there must feel.

Behind no. 30, in another narrow alley, lies the old Baptist chapel and its graveyard by the river, numinous to a degree, which features in "John Halifax, Gentleman", that improving tale.

Before

30 St. Mary's Lane

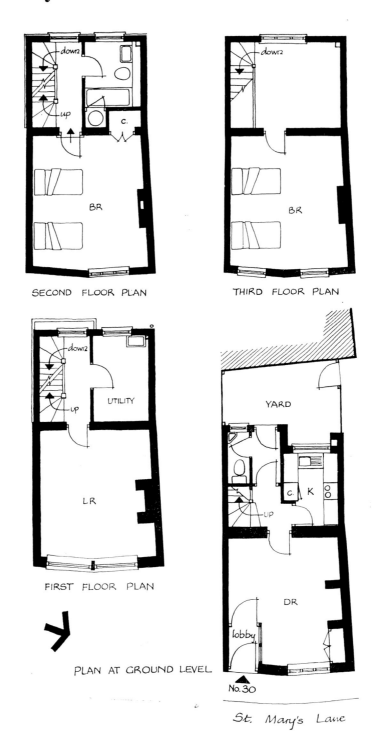

SECOND FLOOR PLAN

THIRD FLOOR PLAN

FIRST FLOOR PLAN

PLAN AT GROUND LEVEL

St. Mary's Lane

The Abbey, the level Ham at the junction of the rivers and, surprisingly, the public baths ("exceptionally good"—Logbook) seem to occupy our visitors; but one party made a geological section of a disused railway cutting ("many layers of Great Oolitic rocks are present") and some others visited the tumulus at Uley known as Hetty Pegler's Tump.

From the logbook

"Lured by the profile of the Malverns seen from the top window, we went there on Christmas Eve and climbed the Herefordshire Beacon".

"We had excellent venison from the fishmonger just by the cross in the centre of town".

"In the Abbey do not miss the back of the vestry door".

"The kitchen is well equipped, except for mugs for hasty drinks".

"Try walking across the Severn Ham in the early morning, discover the Severn, and walk slowly back to enjoy the best possible view of Tewkesbury and the Abbey".

"We met herds of sheep, followed herds of sheep, and visited some more at the Cotswold Farm Park".

"The sermon in the Abbey was short and good".

"Bourton-on-the-Water was full of people—even the stream was".

"We stayed in in the evenings and read the local literature in the admirable small library".

"An evening walk across the broad meadow".

"Despite the fact that it was winter we managed to fill each day to bursting point".

Tower Hill Lodge

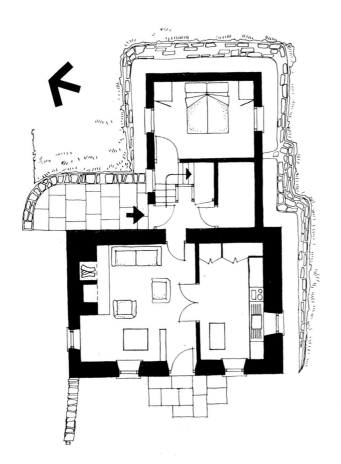

GROUND FLOOR

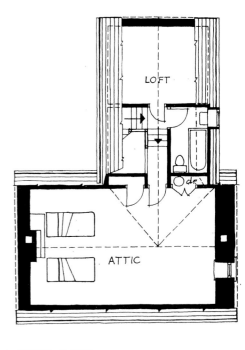

FIRST FLOOR

130

Tower Hill Lodge
Llanarthney, Dyfed

WE ACQUIRED TOWER HILL LODGE as part of a joint scheme with the National Trust to preserve Paxton's Tower and its surroundings. It is an early nineteenth century cottage of well above average quality, solid and rather original in design, looking South over an immense expanse of country (which includes, amongst much else, Llanddarog church, by R. K. Penson, 1860).

It is difficult to imagine a finer view. If however you walk a hundred yards or so up the small green hill behind, to the foot of the Tower, you will come, to your astonishment, on just such a finer view in the opposite direction, surely one of the best in Britain. From here your eye can follow the green windings of the Towy for thirty miles or more.

Paxton's Tower itself was designed by C. R. Cockerell in 1811, ostensibly as a memorial to Nelson but no doubt also (which I should like to have been able to tell the Frenchman quoted below) as a folly and eyecatcher for Middleton Hall, now demolished. Our cottage has rather a modern interior, but an interesting arrangement and a handsome attic.

From the logbook

"We had continuous rain with occasional showers. This was an excellent place to make the best of it".

"Walked up to the Tower (we were nearly blown away) to see the sight of the Towy from Carmarthen to Llandeilo lit by moonlight".

"Cette tour est tres belle et son emplacement est fantastique, mais il est incomprehensible pour un Français qu'elle eut été construite en l'honneur de Lord Nelson".

"On Wednesday morning nine deer were in the wood next to the cottage".

Tower Hill Lodge

"Our most perfect day was a trip to Brianne reservoir. Summer visitors can only guess at the enormous icicles hanging from the rocks and the waterfall completely frozen".

"The boy at the neighbouring farm has a small and engaging but autobiographical sister".

"Have heard a nightingale most evenings".

"Those interested in fossils will find Trilobites (of the Ordovician series) in the many abandoned quarries in the region: I have left a specimen on the chimney piece".

"The local dogs steal any food. They had our steak as we were unpacking".

"On Thursday our quiet was interrupted by traffic and equipment going up to Paxton's Tower. We found out that a BBC Wales programme was being filmed there of Fijian dancers. As their coach could not get up the lane, the Fijians arrived on foot, the men wearing yellow grass skirts and carrying ceremonial spears. With the opportunity of seeing a traditional Fijian dance in the Welsh countryside we abandoned our books and rushed up the hill, where we spent an entertaining afternoon".

". . . the farmer rounding up his sheep on stout mountain pony with aid of whistle and those highly intelligent dogs, fascinating to watch".

"If you enjoy beautiful countryside, and incredible silence, then we think you will enjoy Tower Hill Lodge as we have done".

"Carmarthen Museum, though small, has exciting local finds well displayed, including a lovely gold pendant from the

Pumpsaint mines, and clear explanations of how the Roman mining was done".

"If you like wild and blustery mountain walks, drive up to the filter beds below Llyn y Fan Fach and walk on to the top of Carmarthen Fan — only 2600 ft. but like the Brecon Beacons, seems more. There are baked beans still for tea at the Post Office".

"We found the heronry near Ty-Castell, and spent quite a long time watching the birds returning from the river".

"Carmarthen market is indeed fun. To find it, follow any car with straw sticking out of the back".

"Mother says Eric Gill would have approved of this place".

"We and some of our children spent a very happy fortnight at Tower Hill Lodge, and also very much appreciated the kindness and helpfulness of whosoever we met".

Warden Abbey
Nr. Biggleswade, Bedfordshire

WARDEN ABBEY was Cistercian, founded in 1135 by Walter Espec. The first monks came from Rievaulx. It was dissolved in 1537 and a large house was built on the site by the Gostwick family. At the Dissolution the abbey owned nine manors (two of which went to John Gostwick), besides other land in six counties, and in London, producing an income of £428.6.11½. The seal of the abbey on the deed of surrender bears St. Mary crowned and seated under a canopy, with a sceptre in her left hand and Christ as an infant standing on her knee. On the counter-seal is a crozier between three Warden pears.

Nothing remains above ground of house or abbey except this fragment, of which Mr. Samuel Whitbread has generously given us a long lease. It stands near the buildings of a substantial farm, in a meadow

made uneven by what lies underneath, and is an extremely perplexing building, of very high quality, with plenty about it to interest the antiquary. Clearly it formed part of the Gostwick's house, but it also incorporates part of the abbey; in the course of our repairs a fourteenth century tile pavement emerged, one of the finest and best preserved ever discovered.

The principal room downstairs, which has fine brick-mullioned windows and a high, moulded oak ceiling, seems to have been part of a gallery or broad corridor, with a large open fireplace added later at one end. The spiral stair has solid treads. Occupying the entire first floor is a single room with an early sixteenth century fireplace, an oriel window, and a heavily moulded oak ceiling. It is a pleasure to lie here in bed and wonder for whom such a

Warden Abbey

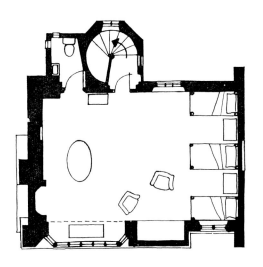

FIRST FLOOR

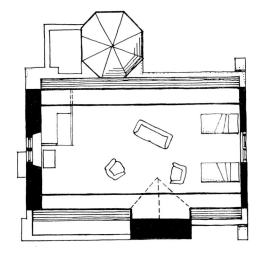

ATTIC

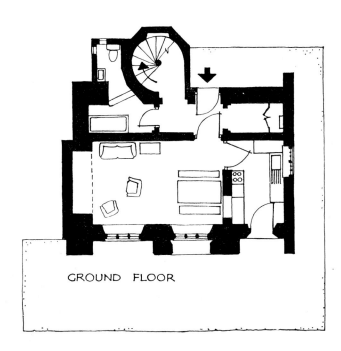

GROUND FLOOR

splendid room can have been constructed. Was it for one of the last abbots; for his guests; or for the Gostwicks? A buttress of the abbey church shows in one corner. Above again is another large room, with an open, wind-braced roof.

The surrounding country has had the advantage of belonging to large landowners and is some of the best in Bedfordshire. Nearby there are two quite exceptional sights—the Shuttleworth Collection of early aircraft, and the vast airship sheds at Cardington built for the R100 and the R101 — both most haunting and evocative of their period.

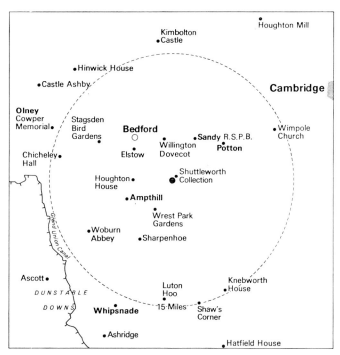

Ty Capel

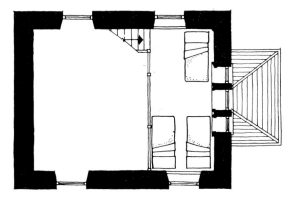

FIRST FLOOR

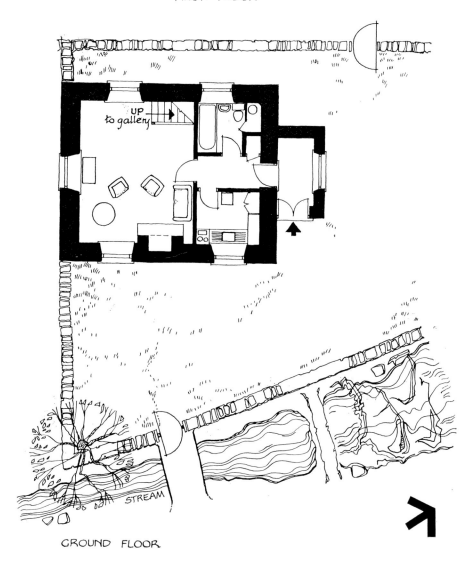

GROUND FLOOR

Ty Capel and Ty Coch
Rhiwddolion, nr. Bettws-y-coed, Gwynedd

RHIWDDOLION is a remote upland at the head of a valley, above Bettws-y-coed. For a time there was a slate quarry and community here, of which interesting traces remain; and long before that Rhiwddolion was on the Roman road, Sarn Elen, which linked the fort near Trawsfynydd with Caerhun in the lower Conway valley, where the coast road ran to Caernarvon. This Elen is supposed to be the mother of the Emperor Constantine, whose father campaigned and died in Britain; and I have wondered whether Edward I, who admired the Eastern Empire, knew of this and designed Caernarvon castle, with its bands of coloured stone, in deliberate imitation of Constantinople.

Now, however, Rhiwddolion, with only three houses left besides ours, is given over to the sheep. It is somewhat hemmed in by the Forestry, and scarred by an insensitive transmission line, but where it

remains open the small-scale landscape of oak trees and rocks emerging from close-cropped pasture is second to none. It is also tranquil and silent except for the sheep and the water; and there is a view far down the valley towards Bettws.

Ty Capel, beside the stream which flows down the valley, was a school-cum-chapel in the days of the slate. It is a robust stone building lined with varnished pine, and at the turn of the century it served a community of 150 people. Ty Coch is a few hundred yards higher up, looking across the head of the valley by a small waterfall. In origin much older than Ty Capel, it has a stone-flagged living room with a large open fireplace. The beam which spans this fireplace is a cruck, re-used no doubt from some earlier house that stood here.

It is almost impossible to get a car to Ty Capel, and quite impossible to get one to Ty Coch; but this has its advantages

137

Ty Capel

since, leaving your car by the forestry track, you can walk up (10 mins., some say longer) through the wood, on the path of enormous half-buried flag-stones, as your predecessors did.

From the logbook

"We came to Ty Capel with the idea of using it as a base to explore North Wales. It exercised its magic on us too, and North Wales went unexplored".

"Ty Capel is very peaceful, the main noise being the sheep".

"It was satisfying to watch the colours of the landscape change as the light changed and as the stones became alternately wet and dry".

"In the evening the Pierces dipped a flock of sheep in the stream outside the chapel".

"When walking to Bettws-y-Coed the quickest route is along the old Roman road, marked 'unsuitable for motors' ".

"Our children speculated for hours on the lives of children in Rhiwddolion. We took great delight in the mosses . . . A perfect place to get to know and understand your family".

"Wear good boots. Take the useless $2\frac{1}{2}''$ map, and compass. If you get lost follow a stream to lower ground. For rescue on mountainside blow 6 blasts on whistle at intervals, if you have a whistle".

"The farmer Mr. Pierce and his family have been most helpful and it has been a great experience to have known them".

"If you come from a city as I do, perhaps you too may feel the same things that I have felt while being here. From the very moment of seeing Ty Capel up until now, the moment when you sit here knowing you have only a few hours left in it, you have the feeling it is yours . . . From the time when you first peer through the window you have the feeling that 'this is just what I want; this is just the way I would have made it' ".

"Snowdon was like Jacob's ladder with coming and going along all the tracks . . . the last fifty yards were like climbing a municipal refuse dump".

"To Lyn Elsi for a picnic lunch with our friends . . . Watched a pair of grey heron . . . Back for birthday dinner at Ty Capel".

"Well we didn't go out much because it's so great here . . . We really love it here, the baby got quite brown".

"If you hear coughings and scratchings at night, it is sheep against the house".

"To my surprise I discovered that I actually quite enjoyed walking".

"We have enjoyed meeting and talking with the Pierces and hope to return one day to this lovely valley".

Ty Capel

"Our last day has been a perfect one— a walk along Sarn Elen and meeting the owner of the whitewashed cottage on the top of the valley".

"We met an old farmer who told us that this chapel was used by the community all around including Bettws and Pont-y-Pant. A minister would visit each week for the service. There were also various activities that took place in the chapel including music festivals. He seemed pleased to revive old memories".

"We had a very enjoyable and busy week discovering the peaceful surroundings which seemed to stretch out for miles in all directions".

"Our last day here . . . We have not been out anywhere. We shall remember this holiday for a long time. Our days have been full and long".

"We leave this house with a little sadness, but hope one day to return".

Ty Coch

From the logbook

"Arrived on a scorching hot day pushing the pram with all our luggage in (wife carrying baby) from Pont-y-Pant station up the Roman Road, Sarn Elen. It was a bit rough in places for the pram, but well worth doing. We've done it every day as we've used the train for our outings".

"Every morning a dipper calls at the pond and he is most fascinating to watch".

"Mr. Pierce told us that when Rhiwddolion ("hill of meadows") was an active village, many of the men used the Roman road daily to catch the train to Blaenau Ffestiniog where they worked in the slate quarries".

"Everything is worth doing here".

"When we arrived the small stream by the wood was so swollen that we couldn't cross at the bridge, so we made a perilous passage along a path which we later realised was the top of a wall. We enjoyed our holiday very much".

"On Christmas Day we walked along the Roman road, Sarn Elen, down to Pont-y-Pant and then up the hill and back".

"A good quartz vein may be seen on the path to Llyn Elsi".

"We spent a very enjoyable afternoon at the sheepdog trials".

"We want to compliment the Landmark Trust on their restoration of these lovely and touching houses".

"Buzzards along the Roman road".

"We have had a very happy week with spectacular gales and squalls of rain which swelled all the streams enormously and caused the waterfall to boil and rage magnificently . . . we have spent the time within walking range of the house and have been very happy doing just that".

"Found Green Hairstreak butterflies in the marshy ground near the stile into the wood".

"Idyllic setting, have not seen the like. Children wonderfully content to be around the waterfall and stream".

"On a clear night, it is worth going outside for five or ten minutes".

". . . there was Ty Capel. It really looked inviting with the light shining through red curtains. I couldn't help looking in through the window; someone was reading on the sofa . . ."

". . . to Bettws-y-Coed, down Sarn Elen, over the Miners' Bridge, and along the river bank".

"We have really enjoyed the log book. The shared experiences make us feel part of a special club".

"We met a previous inhabitant of Rhiwddolion. All the houses were lived in. She went to school in Ty Capel".

"The walks round Ty Coch are so lovely that one does not want to go far away; so with bird watching and wild flower collecting we have been completely happy".

"Bread, baked on the premises and fresh every day, can be obtained at the tiny village of Capel Garmon, high up, with excellent view and a pub in which you may meet a long-retired Chief Petty Officer Roberts, overflowing with reminiscences about the Far East".

"Along Sarn Elen we found a tortoise. We took it to a cottage and found that it is Crwban in Welsh and had been lost for five months".

"We have pottered about locally for most of the week with the exception of a visit to Penmaenmawr and a trip on the Ffestiniog. We have no complaints except that whoever is reading this is here, and we are not".

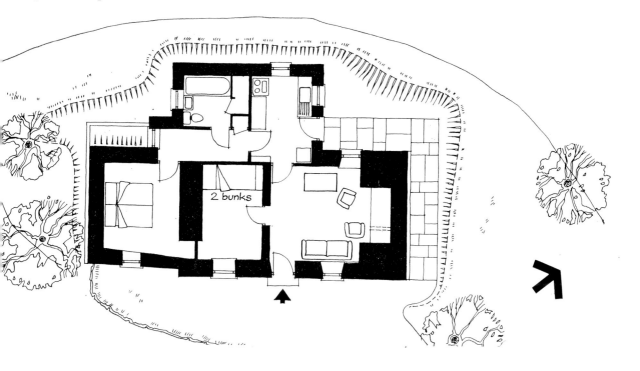

2 bunks

Wellbrook Beetling Mill

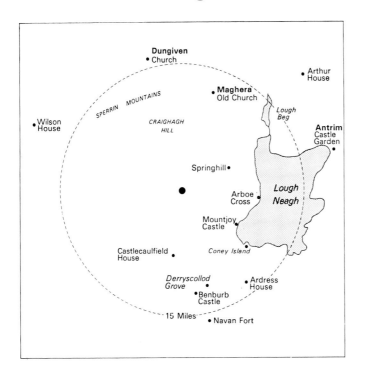

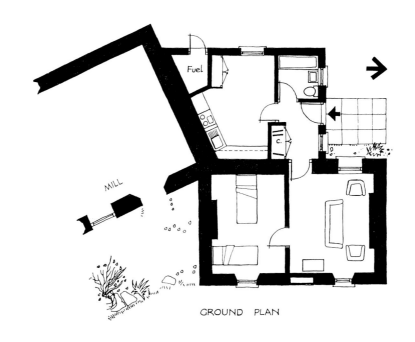

GROUND PLAN

Wellbrook Beetling Mill
Cookstown, Co. Tyrone, N. Ireland

BEETLING IS THE final process in the manufacture of linen, when the cloth is hammered to produce a sheen, and this water powered beetling mill is the only one in Ireland preserved in working order. It was built in 1765 by the Faulkner family and holds seven beetling engines with a conditioning loft above. The National Trust acquired it in 1968. We provided the balance of money needed for its restoration after a public appeal, and have taken a long lease of the manager's cottage.

Wellbrook, with its mill, mill leat and dam, and little river running among trees, has a special quality, being simultaneously picturesque and technical, functional and beautiful, as much in Britain was — and perhaps again could be. For those who wish to discover this agreeable uncrowded land it is a pleasant place to stay.

The West Blockhouse
Dale, Dyfed

THIS IS THE OUTERMOST WORK of the mid-nineteenth century fortifications of Milford Haven. It consisted of a single battery of five heavy guns commanding the entrance to the harbour, with defensible granite barracks.

Since we bought it and the headland behind (on which are remains of emplacements for later 9·2 inch guns) our resources for this kind of work have been devoted to Fort Clonque, and the West Blockhouse has had to wait; but we hope in due course to restore it, so that hardy spirits may stay in this remote and vertiginous spot, and savour the view down the coast of Pembrokeshire — with the spectacle every so often of a really big tanker feeling its way through the mouth of the haven at one's feet.

Tixall Gatehouse
Nr. Stafford

AS THE TRAVELLER by canal comes down the valley of the Sow, and through Tixall lock, he enters the last and most beautiful mile of the Staffordshire and Worcestershire Canal before its junction with the Trent and Mersey. The cut here broadens into a lake, known to boaters as Tixall Wide. On either side lie most handsome stretches of country — to the South, Shugborough, with Cannock Chase beyond, and, to the North, Ingestre, with Tixall Gatehouse in the foreground. This was built about 1580 by Sir Walter Aston, who was knighted for his bravery at the siege of Leith — one of the few occasions before the Union when Scotland fought with the English against the French. His son had just married the daughter of Sir Thomas Lucy (Shakespeare's Justice Shallow) of Charlecote, where there is an earlier gatehouse which may have inspired the much grander one at Tixall.

For some reason the Astons seem to have been extremely rich. The table at Tixall "was magnificently served — three courses the year about, and twenty dishes at each course. The twenty serving men who carried the dishes affected to stamp louder than was needed, which made a noise like thunder every course that was carried up ... Behind my Lord's chair stood every day his gentleman, his house steward, his chief park-keeper, and a footman ready to fetch the guests what my Lord called for ... He was very curious in his wines".

The Tudor house, in front of which the gatehouse stood, was replaced in the eighteenth century by another house built to one side of it by Thomas Clifford, a descendant of the Astons. In this, and in his landscape works, he was "assisted by the taste and judgement of the celebrated Brown". Both these houses

145

Tixall Gatehouse

have disappeared, and the gate-house is today surrounded by grass. It was described by Erdeswick in 1598 as "one of the fairest pieces of work made of late times that I have seen in all these countries" and, more recently, as "an Elizabethan ruin, without roof, floors or windows, standing in a field and used as a shelter for cattle". It is magnificent and exceptional in every respect — design, materials and execution.

We bought the building in 1968 when the last parts of Lord Shrewsbury's estate were being sold. The first floor appears to have been a single enormous room; there was no sign of sub-division and only one fireplace, with traces of a very large chimneypiece. We have divided

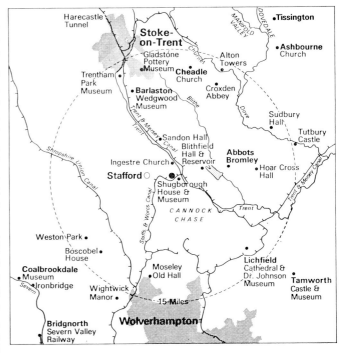

Tixall Gatehouse

this space into five large rooms, one of which forms a gallery with an oriel window at each end above the two archways. In the spandrels of these archways are, facing the outside world, armed warriors; and, on the inside, voluptuous ladies thinly disguised as angels. The second floor we have left empty. The roof we have re-paved with stone, and to be high up here among the balustrades and turret tops, with Arcadian landscape on every hand, is yet another important Landmark Trust experience. The gatehouse clock lives in one of the turrets; this strikes the hour, and perhaps the half hour, but has no hands or face to

show the actual time, which here seems unimportant, even vulgar.

Mary Queen of Scots was imprisoned here for about a fortnight after the Babington conspiracy in 1586, shortly before her removal to Fotheringay — also a beautiful spot — where she was beheaded. Thirty years later her son James I stayed here for two days. In 1678 Tixall, by then a Catholic house, played a part in the Titus Oates conspiracy; the Aston of the day was committed to the Tower for seven years and Lord Stafford, accused of plotting at Tixall, was executed.

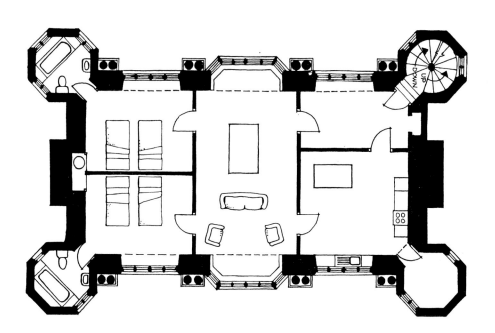

The Master's House
Chadwick Street, Longton, Stoke-on-Trent

THE GLADSTONE POTTERY MUSEUM, with which we have had friendly relations since the beginning, are giving us a long lease of this ordinary but important house. It is not very quiet, and the view is terrible, but we can promise unimaginable sensations here to anyone who finds the Potteries as genuine and moving as we do. The Master's House backs on to a group of bottle ovens, almost the last survivors of their kind, from which for so long, and with such dirt and toil, emerged such beautiful and useful things. In the museum, which is a living and imaginative one, it is possible to study the history of colours and glazes, to enter the ovens themselves, and to see how "china" was and is made.

Instead of beaches and the sea, there is the Trent and Mersey canal, whose passage through Stoke on Trent, via the Shelton Bar ironworks and, eventually, the Harecastle tunnel, is quite specially dramatic. Outside Stoke, along the Trent valley, there are one or two really good houses to visit; and in the evening there is Arnold Bennett, or bingo amid the late nineteenth century baroque plasterwork of the Empire in Longton, an important provincial theatre which it must be hoped will survive.

The Master's House

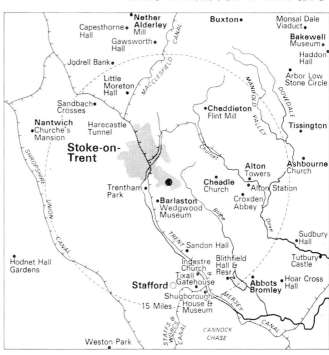

The Master's House

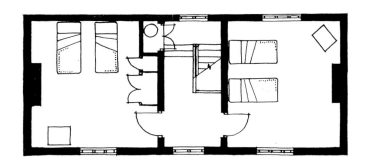

FIRST FLOOR

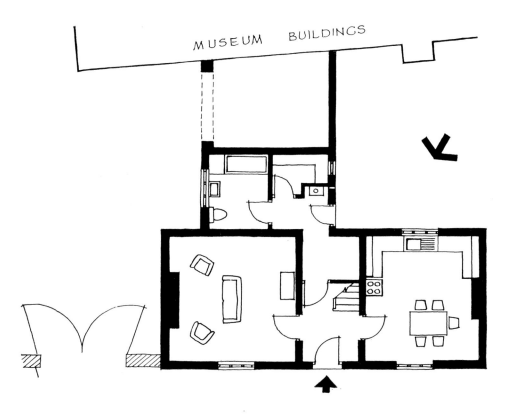

MUSEUM BUILDINGS

GROUND FLOOR

150

Woodspring Priory
Kewstoke, Weston-super-Mare, Avon

WE BOUGHT WOODSPRING PRIORY in 1969 as part of a joint scheme with the National Trust, who raised money to buy the surrounding coastal land at the same time. The priory was founded in 1210 by William de Courtenay, grandson of Reginald FitzUrse who, with other west countrymen, murdered Thomas à Becket. It was an Augustinian house, of the rule of St. Victor (rare in England), dedicated to the Trinity, St. Mary and St. Thomas the Martyr.

Woodspring does not seem to have flourished particularly except, as elsewhere in Somerset, during the fifteenth century, when the tower and nave of the church, the infirmary, and the great barn (still used for its original purpose) were built of a beautiful golden stone. The north aisle of the church was not quite finished when, in September 1536, the priory was suppressed and the church, most unusually, turned into a house, with chimney stacks built up through the roof of the nave. In 1918 the owner intended to make the church a hotel, surrounded by a "bungalow town", but this never came to anything, and we found Woodspring as it had been since the Dissolution, the church still inhabited as the farmhouse of a picturesque and rather old-fashioned farm.

However, the buildings had suffered greatly from the ravages of time and

151

Woodspring Priory

*Alterations to
Curator's house,* 1976

Woodspring Priory

violence. The tower of the church, with truly enormous trunks of ivy bursting the stones apart, was repaired for us by J. Dawson & Sons of Bristol, employing one man and a boy, using, even in this exposed place, vertical ladders instead of scaffolding. The result is the best piece of work done for us anywhere — indeed it is almost impossible to tell that anything has been done at all. We have also repaired the infirmary, taking down and reassembling (for the second time in its history) the early fifteenth century arched-brace collar beam roof with three tiers of windbraces, and building a ring beam into the top of the walls. Otherwise we have left the infirmary as we found it, with an earth floor and open to sheep and cattle.

We have also removed many sheds, poles and wires; have moved a Dutch barn; and have de-modernised the old cottage in which our curator lives by removing the steel window frames and putting back its pantiled roof. There is still much to do, but we hope that in the end it will be possible once again to live in the church, with its large tranquil rooms, and in the domestic wing rebuilt in 1701.

Meanwhile we have published a guide

book; and have opened to the public (daylight hours, never closed) the church, the infirmary, and the orchard which adjoins both, in which you may picnic and speculate what lies beneath the humpy green cloth of its surface.

Other monastic remains are grander, others more complete than Woodspring, but few have kept so well the serene atmosphere of an isolated religious community, surrounded by a working farm, and lying next to the sea.

Wortham Manor
Nr. Lifton, Launceston, Devon

THIS IS A MEDIEVAL HOUSE of the highest quality, inherited and enlarged early in the fifteenth century by the Dinhams, who were one of the great Norman families of Devon (they came from Dinant). A few changes were made over the next hundred years, but since then it has been left entirely unaltered in every respect, its successive owners being neither too rich nor too poor. The doors, windows and fireplaces are of dressed granite, a noble and intractable material seen to great advantage here.

The hall, with an open arched-brace roof, is very like that at Cotehele — another quite exceptional medieval house, but a good deal grander, further down the Tamar valley. An upper floor has been made in the hall, but here it was done earlier than usual, at the very end of the middle ages, and with great care.

As a result the medieval screens and spere survive, and the oak ceiling of the lower hall has heavily moulded beams and rich late Gothic carving, with no sign of Renaissance influence. These alterations were made by John Dinham, perhaps with money from his rich cousin Thomasine of Week St. Mary, who had a regard for him (see p. 16). In 1533, then an old man, he begged to be excused from accepting a knighthood.

The house has had to be entirely re-roofed (taking the opportunity to recover its original plan) and we have had to do much else. Indeed Wortham has cost us more than any other building that we own. However it has been undeniably worth it and those who stay here have an unrivalled opportunity to study and experience the middle ages — for example their simplicity (in some things), solidity,

155

and lack of privacy (there are no passages, all the rooms lead out of each other). We have now also managed to buy the disused farm buildings on two sides of the house so that its setting can be preserved.

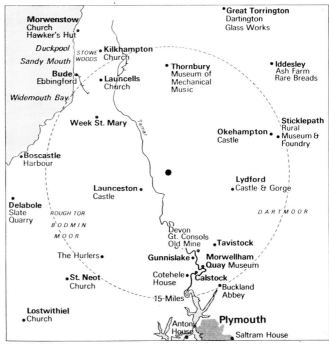

Wortham Manor

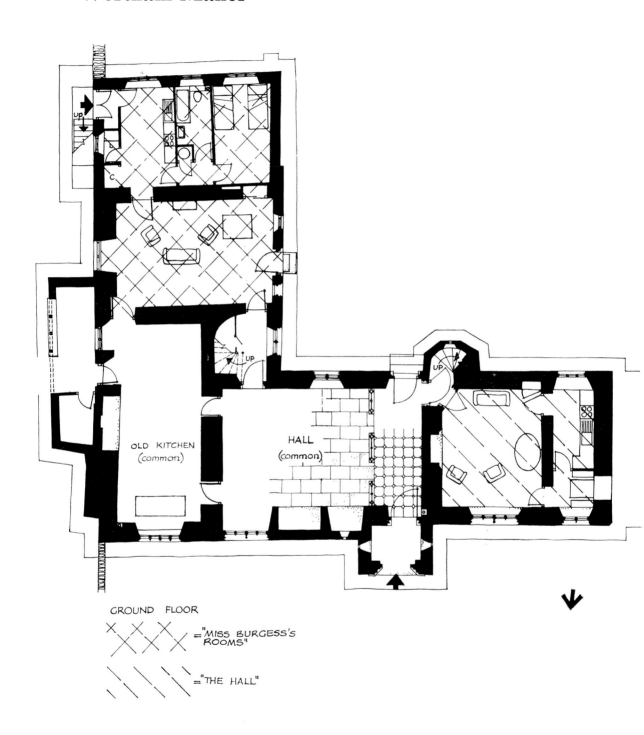

OLD KITCHEN
(common)

HALL
(common)

UP

UP

UP

GROUND FLOOR

XXXX = "MISS BURGESS'S ROOMS"

///// = "THE HALL"

158

Wortham Manor

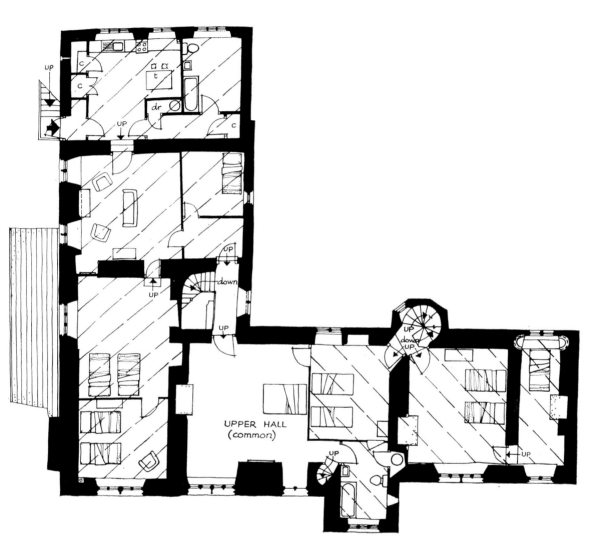

UPPER HALL
(common)

FIRST FLOOR

 = "THE OLD SOLAR"

= "THE HALL"

159

The Manifold paid to establish HMS *Belfast* in the Pool of London and has made small contributions to her upkeep since. To put this latter-day castle of steel opposite our most famous castle of stone seemed to us a bold and heartening idea, far more than just a piece of preservation. Here she will be to all a permanent reminder of the sea, of the world beyond the sea, and of the virtues of courage and service.

The Manifold Trust

Secretary: Miss Christine Gilbertson, 1 Smith Square, London, S.W.1.

Distributions 1963-1976

	£000	%
Churches	43	
Other buildings, etc.	2,799	74
HMS *Belfast*	105	
The Maritime Trust	180	
HMS *Unicorn*	11	
SS *Great Britain*	15	
Other ships, etc.	33	
The Sail Training Association	1	9
The Ryhope Engines Trust	1	
The Gladstone Pottery	20	
The Lilleshall Beam Blowing Engines	12	
The Iron Bridge	50	
Woodbridge Tide Mill	5	
Other projects for industrial preservation	4	2
The Upper Avon Navigation	21	
The Kennet and Avon Canal	50	
Other navigations	16	2
Nottingham University (pollution research)	8	
Other environmental projects	6	
Education	25	
The London Library	5	
The National Gallery (Titian Appeal)	5	
The Bate Benefaction (historic musical instruments)	5	
The Royal Marines Museum	1	
The National Army Museum	1	
The Victorian Society	8	
Playing fields, halls, etc.	44	
General welfare	20	3
Gifts to commercial firms made by Government order*	220	6
Administration	138	4
	3,852	100

These figures include £19,930 distributed from a small trust with the same origins and policy.

* One of many harmful effects of the ill-conceived and retrospective Counter Inflation Order 1972.

Architects and Builders

Architects

K. M. Benbow:	Hole Cottage
L. H. Bond:	Tixall Gatehouse
David Brain & Stollar:	Marshal Wade's House
Burrough & Hannam:	Woodspring Priory
D. Carr and S. Tod:	The Pineapple; Saddell Castle
H. Creighton:	The Gothic Temple
M. and S. Gooch:	Appleton Water Tower
R. Gradidge:	Alton Station
Donald W. Insall & Associates:	45 Cloth Fair
P. Jebb:	Fort Clonque; Lundy
A. Miles:	Clytha Castle
C. H. P. Pearn:	The College; Coombe; The Danescombe Mine; The Egyptian House; Margells; Sanders; Wortham Manor
Charles B. Pearson & Partners:	The Music Room
J. Phillips:	Warden Abbey
M. T. Pritchard:	Plas Uchaf
H. G. Raggett	30 St. Mary's Lane
G. Robb:	Edale Mill; 34 High Street Ironbridge; The Master's House; North Street, Cromford
J. Schofield:	The Old Hall
L. Beddall Smith:	The Bath Tower; Church Cottage; Tower Hill Lodge; 15 Tower Hill; Ty Capel; Ty Coch
J. Warren	The Martello Tower; The New Inn; Purton Green

Principal Quantity Surveyor: T. G. Williams, F.R.I.C.S.

Principal Builders

George Bale & Sons:	Coombe
Robert Beatson & Son:	The Pineapple; Saddell Castle
Campbell & Smith Ltd:	Saddell Castle
J. Dawson & Sons	Woodspring Priory
Ernest Deacon Ltd:	Old Radnor
Fisher & Sons Ltd:	Appleton Water Tower
Forresters of Alton:	Alton Station
E. L. Greening & Sons:	The Danescombe Mine; Wortham Manor
J. Kenneth Hughes Ltd:	Plas Uchaf; Ty Capel; Ty Coch
Lewis Jackson Ltd:	North Street, Cromford
Wm. C. Reade Ltd:	The Martello Tower; The New Inn
J. G. Rees & Sons:	Tower Hill Lodge
F. Rendell & Sons:	Marshal Wade's House
Sandy & Co. Ltd:	Tixall Gatehouse
Clement Theobald & Sons Ltd:	Purton Green
J. Trivett & Co. Ltd:	Margells
Bernard Ward Ltd:	Warden Abbey
H. & E. Waters Ltd:	Hole Cottage

Would you be willing take part in the work of the Landmark Trust? We are seeking thoughtful and dependable people to act as paid, part-time

LOCAL SECRETARIES

The task would be to represent us locally; and also to help keep up our standards by visiting every month one (or more) of our places, arranging any household maintenance outside the province of our caretaker.

If you are one of those people who take trouble with their own homes; if you live within fifteen miles of any of our places, and have an hour or two a week to spare; and if you would get satisfaction from seeing that our visitors enjoy themselves — then please write to the General Secretary.

ACKNOWLEDGEMENTS: The Landmark Trust is grateful for the use of photographs as follows: Messrs. Pearn and Proctor 103; John Mills Ltd., Liverpool 82, 84, 164; G. Robb 34, 148; W. R. Williams 16, 28, 69 101, 117, 125; K. C. Mason 24; O. F. Clarke 11; D. Sach 54, 58; C. M. Smith 60, 155; J. Warren 80, 86, 87, 89; National Monuments Record 145; C. D. Crook 152; Bedfordshire County Council 133, 135; S. Chenies 46; S. Pollitzer 1, 3, 68, 105, 157; William Salt Library 6; T. A. Dulake 33, 71, 72, 78, 112, 121, 135, 50 (exteriors); Country Life 95; Donald Insall, Architects 12; J. F. London 154, 156; D. Carpenter 26, 29, 97; A. R. Bultitude 19, 137; Aerofilms 8, 18, 75; S. M. Smith 22; J. L. E. Smith 7, 13, 38, 43, 83, 139; R. D. Moulton 56; West Air Photography, Weston-super-Mare 151; Stewart Bale Ltd. 109; The Controller of Her Majesty's Stationery Office 108; S. M. Rolt 15, 34 (interiors), 48, 49, 50 (interior), 89 (interior), 92 110, 129; G. Clarke 80; C. H. P. Pearn 36; Barbican Photographic 99; A. Leach 114; Dr. G. A. Matthews 64, 79; Staffordshire County Council 4; N. Jones 111; The Gladstone Pottery 149; W. Procter 37; M. D. Gilbert 31;

Frontispiece, A. De Rahm.

The quotation on p. 41 is reprinted by permission of Messrs. Faber and Faber from "The Pebbles on the Beach" by Clarence Ellis.

The maps were compiled by Mrs C. Ridley and drawn by Fairey Surveys Ltd.

The plans are by Desmond Thomas.

From the Music Room ceiling

PRINTED BY TITUS WILSON & SON LTD., 28 HIGHGATE, KENDAL, CUMBRIA